# Global Tales

## Stories from many cultures

Selected and edited by Chris Donovan,
Alun Hicks and Beverley Naidoo

General editor: Michael Marland
Series consultant: Geoff Barton

LONGMAN

## Longman Imprint Books
General Editor: Michael Marland

### New Titles
*Characters from Pre-20th Century Novels*
*Diaries and Letters*
*Highlights from 19th-Century Novels*
*Stories from Europe*
*Ten Short Plays*
*Travel Writing*
*Genres*
*Landmarks*
*Scenes from Plays*
*Stories from Africa*
*Two Centuries*

### Previously published titles
*Autobiographies*
*Cider with Rosie* Laurie Lee
*The Diary of Anne Frank* edited by Christopher Martin
*Ghost Stories* selected by Susan Hill
*The Human Element and other stories* Stan Barstow
*I'm the King of the Castle* Susan Hill
*P'tang, Yang, Kipperbang and other TV plays* Jack Rosenthal
*A Roald Dahl Selection*
*Stories from Asia*
*The Woman in Black* Susan Hill

Narrative Styles:
— Ironic title? Ending?
1) Irony
2) Humour
3) Narrator — seasons, title, objects
4) Symbolism
5) Metaphor
6) Personifica / Alliteray Juxtaposin
7) Repitin
8) Inner thoughts ←
9) Way Story Starts & ends
10) Dialogue
11) Punctuan.

12) Names
13) Flashbacks
14) Contrast
15) Title
16) How it Starts/Ends
   → in ā middle of thought etc.
17) Surprise element
18) Setting
19) Pt. of view ⇒ narrator's voice
20) Stream of consciousness
   ⇒ without word 4 ?
21) Lang. ⇒ choice of word
22) Paragraphing
23) Interior monologue.
24) Free & Open Discourse
25) Foreshadowing

# Contents

········

*Handwritten notes: Questions cld be asked: o Theme o Characterisation + Self-responses. o Stylistic devices.*

*Handwritten note: know at least 4 stories. well.*

iii

# CONTENTS

## Focus on context

## Focus on language

## Focus on theme

*Q^n:* With close ref. to ē text, how explain how do u feel towards about Robert's actions towards a dog.

① What did R. do 2 ē dog?

② Why do u feel... the R's ac^n?

③ What do u feel...

# The National Curriculum

The well-read person should be familiar with the range of literature in English from across the English-speaking world. This is strongly stated in the requirements of the National Curriculum: 'Pupils should read texts from other cultures and traditions that represent their distinctive voices and forms, and offer varied perspectives and subject matter.' The seventeen short stories that Beverley Naidoo, Alun Hicks and Chris Donovan have brought together from the literature of the modern world to make this diverse collection certainly meet that important requirement. They are indeed 'Stories from many cultures' in which 'our' and 'other' overlap.

The short story is particularly suited to demonstrating the work of 'major writers with well-established critical reputations, whose works were published after 1900', as required by the National Curriculum. Indeed, the short story has been one of the great literary traditions of this century. Two stories are published here for the first time, but the majority of the writers are internationally praised major writers, mostly with special acclaim for their short stories. For instance, Anita Desai, from India, whose father was Bengali; Mikhail Bulgakov, from Kiev in the Ukraine; Julius Lester, from Missouri, USA, and Bernard MacLaverty, from Northern Ireland. Graham Greene compared R. K. Narayan, who was born in Madras in India, to the great Russian short-story writer, Chekhov, who could be thought of as the creator of the modern short-story tradition.

By bringing together such a diversity of writers, the collection can not only meet the demanding requirement of 'other cultures and traditions', but is also shaped to meet the requirement that 'Novels and short stories selected should . . . include a range of narrative structures and literary techniques; extend pupils' ideas and their moral and emotional understanding; offer perspectives on society and community and their impact on the lives of individuals; show the variety of language use in fiction'. With grouping of stories to stimulate a comparative approach, *Global Tales* meets all these requirements.

*Michael Marland*

# Introduction

English is a world language and some of the most exciting writing in English today comes from around the world. This collection, including two stories translated into English, offers you an opportunity to experience some of this global diversity.

The short story is wonderfully versatile. Like a necklace it can take many shapes while always needing a firm thread or structure to link one end to the other. You will find a variety of forms here, with writers using many different ways of telling their tales. There is also rich variety in how the English language itself is used. As for themes, there are stories to extend and challenge ideas and understanding about people, as well as sometimes their wider societies and environments. Some stories enter settings and subjects which you may immediately recognise. Others will carry you beyond your own direct experience.

Some of the writers are well-known internationally while others are less familiar. Two stories (*What Do You Do in Winter?* and *Poinsettias*) have not been published before. The fact that stories across the world are being written in, or translated into, English immediately indicates the linking of cultures. If you read other works by these writers (see Further reading) you will begin to hear how each has a distinctively individual voice with a particular way of using and shaping language.

The stories have been grouped to help compare particular aspects but this arrangement is just one way of approaching them. Stories in one section may well spark off ideas about those in another. We chose them with thirteen to sixteen year olds in mind and some are easier to read than others. However, even the more simply written stories have got deeper layers to talk and think about.

For **Plot**, we have two stories where the plot hinges on knowledge. In *An Astrologer's Day* the main character knows something we don't until the very end, while in *The Pieces of Silver* we finally learn something with the central character which leads into a double twist.

For **Character**, the stories focus on relationships between adults and children. In *Crime and Punishment* the reader looks on with the storyteller from the outside, while in *Warrior Woman* and *The Easter Hat* a mother is viewed through the eyes of her child.

Under **Setting**, a sense of place is essential to each story: Stradbroke Island off the Queensland Coast in *Kill to Eat*; a small Welsh town in *What Do You Do in Winter?*; and a remote Russian province in *The Steel Windpipe*.

Under **Context**, we explore wider historical, political and social contexts. There is Mississippi in the 1930s in *The Gold Cadillac* and South Africa under apartheid in *Poinsettias*. In *Robert and the Dog*, a seemingly simple story leads to much deeper questions about how Europe connects to Africa. That relationship also lurks in the powerfully disturbing story *The Man*.

For a focus on **Language**, *Why Apes Look Like People* stems from the oral tradition of the American South with its roots in African folk tale. *Full Stop* is told through letters between a Caribbean grandmother and her granddaughter in New York. *The Escape*, set in London, is vibrantly told through standard and Jamaican English.

Ending with **Theme**, both *Circus Cat Alley Cat* and *More than just the Disease* are to do with childhood perceptions.

Of course features such as plot, character, setting, context, language and theme are part and parcel of most stories and closely intertwined. We hope you will find many new and interesting ways of making your own connections with these global tales.

*Chris Donovan, Alun Hicks and Beverley Naidoo*

# Focus on plot

## An Astrologer's Day

**by R. K. Narayan**

Punctually at midday he opened his bag and spread out his professional equipment, which consisted of a dozen cowrie shells, a square piece of cloth with obscure mystic charts on it, a notebook and a bundle of palmyra writing. His forehead was resplendent with sacred ash and vermilion, and his eyes sparkled with a sharp abnormal gleam which was really an outcome of a continual searching look for customers, but which his simple clients took to be a prophetic light and felt comforted. The power of his eyes was considerably enhanced by their position – placed as they were between the painted forehead and the dark whiskers which streamed down his cheeks: even a half-wit's eyes would sparkle in such a setting. To crown the effect he wound a saffron-coloured turban around his head. This colour scheme never failed. People were attracted to him as bees are attracted to cosmos or dahlia stalks. He sat under the boughs of a spreading tamarind tree which flanked a path running through the Town Hall Park. It was a remarkable place in many ways: a surging crowd was always moving up and down this narrow road morning till night. A variety of trades and

1

occupations was represented all along its way: medicine-sellers, sellers of stolen hardware and junk, magicians and, above all, an auctioneer of cheap cloth, who created enough din all day to attract the whole town. Next to him in vociferousness came a vendor of fried groundnuts, who gave his ware a fancy name each day, calling it Bombay Ice-Cream one day, and on the next Delhi Almond, and on the third Raja's Delicacy, and so on and so forth, and people flocked to him. A considerable portion of his crowd dallied before the astrologer too. The astrologer transacted his business by the light of a flare which crackled and smoked up above the groundnut heap nearby. Half the enchantment of the place was due to the fact that it did not have the benefit of municipal lighting. The place was lit up by shop lights. One or two had hissing gaslights, some had naked flares stuck on poles, some were lit up by old cycle lamps and one or two, like the astrologer's, managed without lights of their own. It was a bewildering criss-cross of light rays and moving shadows. This suited the astrologer very well, for the simple reason that he had not in the least intended to be an astrologer when he began life; and he knew no more of what was going to happen to others than he knew what was going to happen to himself next minute. He was as much a stranger to the stars as were his innocent customers. Yet he said things which pleased and astonished everyone: that was more a matter of study, practice and shrewd guess-work. All the same, it was as much an honest man's labour as any other, and he deserved the wages he carried home at the end of a day.

He had left his village without any previous thought or plan. If he had continued there he would have carried on the work of his forefathers – namely, tilling

2

the land, living, marrying and ripening in his cornfield and ancestral home. But that was not to be. He had to leave home without telling anyone, and he could not rest till he left it behind a couple of hundred miles. To a villager it is a great deal, as if an ocean flowed between.

He had a working analysis of mankind's troubles: marriage, money and the tangles of human ties. Long practice had sharpened his perception. Within five minutes he understood what was wrong. He charged three pies per question and never opened his mouth till the other had spoken for at least ten minutes, which provided him enough stuff for a dozen answers and advices. When he told the person before him, gazing at his palm, 'In many ways you are not getting the fullest results for your efforts,' nine out of ten were disposed to agree with him. Or he questioned: 'Is there any woman in your family, maybe even a distant relative, who is not well disposed towards you?' Or he gave an analysis of character: 'Most of your troubles are due to your nature. How can you be otherwise with Saturn where he is? You have an impetuous nature and a rough exterior.' This endeared him to their hearts immediately, for even the mildest of us loves to think that he has a forbidding exterior.

The nuts-vendor blew out his flare and rose to go home. This was a signal for the astrologer to bundle up too, since it left him in darkness except for a little shaft of green light which strayed in from somewhere and touched the ground before him. He picked up his cowrie shells and paraphernalia and was putting them back into his bag when the green shaft of light was blotted out; he looked up and saw a man standing before him. He sensed a possible client and said: 'You look so careworn. It will do you good to sit down for a while and chat with me.' The other grumbled some

3

vague reply. The astrologer pressed his invitation; whereupon the other thrust his palm under his nose, saying: 'You call yourself an astrologer?' The astrologer felt challenged and said, tilting the other's palm towards the green shaft of light: 'Yours is a nature . . .' 'Oh, stop that,' the other said. 'Tell me something worthwhile . . .'

Our friend felt piqued. 'I charge only three pies per question, and what you get ought to be good enough for your money . . .' At this the other withdrew his arm, took out an anna and flung it out to him, saying, 'I have some questions to ask. If I prove you are bluffing, you must return that anna to me with interest.'

'If you find my answers satisfactory, will you give me five rupees?'

'No.'

'Or will you give me eight annas?'

'All right, provided you give me twice as much if you are wrong,' said the stranger. This pact was accepted after a little further argument. The astrologer sent up a prayer to heaven as the other lit a cheroot. The astrologer caught a glimpse of his face by the match-light. There was a pause as cars hooted on the road, jutka-drivers swore at their horses and the babble of the crowd agitated the semi-darkness of the park. The other sat down, sucking his cheroot, puffing out, sat there ruthlessly. The astrologer felt very uncom-fortable. 'Here, take your anna back. I am not used to such challenges. It is late for me today . . .' He made preparations to bundle up. The other held his wrist and said, 'You can't get out of it now. You dragged me in while I was passing.' The astrologer shivered in his grip; and his voice shook and became faint. 'Leave me today. I will speak to you tomorrow.' The other thrust his palm in his face and said, 'Challenge is challenge.

4

Go on.' The astrologer proceeded with his throat drying up. 'There is a woman . . .'

'Stop,' said the other. 'I don't want all that. Shall I succeed in my present search or not? Answer this and go. Otherwise I will not let you go till you disgorge all your coins.' The astrologer muttered a few incantations and replied, 'All right. I will speak. But will you give me a rupee if what I say is convincing? Otherwise I will not open my mouth, and you may do what you like.' After a good deal of haggling the other agreed. The astrologer said, 'You were left for dead. Am I right?'

'Ah, tell me more.'

'A knife has passed through you once?' said the astrologer.

'Good fellow!' He bared his chest to show the scar. 'What else?'

'And then you were pushed into a well nearby in the field. You were left for dead.'

'I should have been dead if some passer-by had not chanced to peep into the well,' exclaimed the other, overwhelmed by enthusiasm. 'When shall I get at him?' he asked, clenching his fist.

'In the next world,' answered the astrologer. 'He died four months ago in a far-off town. You will never see any more of him.' The other groaned on hearing it. The astrologer proceeded.

'Guru Nayak –'

'You know my name!' the other said, taken aback.

'As I know all other things. Guru Nayak, listen carefully to what I have to say. Your village is two days' journey due north of this town. Take the next train and be gone. I see once again great danger to your life if you go from home.' He took out a pinch of sacred ash and held it out to him. 'Rub it on your forehead and go home. Never travel southward again,

5

R. K. NARAYAN

and you will live to be a hundred.'

'Why should I leave home again?' the other said reflectively. 'I was only going away now and then to look for him and to choke out his life if I met him.' He shook his head regretfully. 'He has escaped my hands. I hope at least he died as he deserved.' 'Yes,' said the astrologer. 'He was crushed under a lorry.' The other looked gratified to hear it. *pacified.*

The place was deserted by the time the astrologer picked up his articles and put them into his bag. The green shaft was also gone, leaving the place in darkness and silence. The stranger had gone off into the night, after giving the astrologer a handful of coins.

It was nearly midnight when the astrologer reached home. His wife was waiting for him at the door and demanded an explanation. He flung the coins at her and said, 'Count them. One man gave all that.'

'Twelve and a half annas,' she said, counting. She was overjoyed. 'I can buy some *jaggery* and coconut tomorrow. The child has been asking for sweets for so many days now. I will prepare some nice stuff for her.'

'The swine has cheated me! He promised me a rupee,' said the astrologer. She looked up at him. 'You look worried. What is wrong?'  *why worried*

'Nothing.'

After dinner, sitting on the *pyol*, he told her, 'Do you know a great load is gone from me today? I thought I had the blood of a man on my hands all these years. That was the reason why I ran away from home, settled here and married you. He is alive.'  *relieve  escapism*

She gasped. 'You tried to kill!'

'Yes, in our village, when I was a silly youngster. We drank, gambled and quarrelled badly one day – why think of it now? Time to sleep,' he said, yawning, and stretched himself on the *pyol*.

6  Husband + wife
   relationship → not close as astro. did
                  not confide in wife

# The Pieces of Silver

**by Karl Sealy**

When, at five minutes to ten, the bell started to ring, a pall of silence settled over the noisy playfield.

Reluctantly games of cricket and pick-ups were abandoned; climbers came slithering down from the old tamarind tree on the school grounds or dropped quickly from its branches, making haste to clear their mouths of the green, acid fruit they had been enjoying.

The school of four hundred odd boys assembled in ranks across the pebbled playfield, waiting for inspection before they could file into the red-walled school. Some glanced apprehensively at their dusty, naked feet, while others tried feverishly to make their nails and hands presentable.

The teachers came from the schoolroom in a leisurely bunch, laughing and joking in quiet voices as they sauntered towards the boys.

The stout, pompous, acting Headmaster came to the window that opened off his platform on to the playfield, still making an unnecessary clangour with his bell, and looked sternly over the assembled rows of scholars. The smaller boys straightened and stiffened under his cold gaze.

As the teachers passed slowly along the ranks the boys turned their hands back and forth and grinned to show their teeth. A number of boys who failed to pass the teachers' inspection of health were hauled out of the ranks and ordered in to the acting Head. There were three strokes with his cane of plaited tamarind stalks for unclean hands; four for improperly brushed teeth and six for an uncombed head.

After the inspection the boys filed quietly into school and to their different classes. When you could have heard a pin drop the schoolmaster rapped out the order: 'Shun!' The entire school of boys flung their hands to their foreheads and chanted: 'Good morning to our teachers.'

The schoolmaster announced a hymn, and emitting an untrue, faltering note, invited the scholars to take it. The boys rendered a rich improvement of the sound, and when the schoolmaster flung his hand up and stamped his foot they tore full-throatedly into the hymn.

At the conclusion of the hymn the boys sang, 'Amen,' bringing their hands up to their faces in an attitude of prayer. The schoolmaster submitted a long, impromptu supplication, rambling and ill-worded, at the end of which the boys said 'Amen' once more. Again the schoolmaster ordered: 'Shun!' The boys came to attention, and school was ready to begin.

But this morning the schoolmaster did not order the school to be seated as was the normal custom after prayers. Instead he fixed the school with his cold eyes and said:

'Those who have brought contributions to Mr Megahey's purse will give them to their teachers.'

Hands delved into pockets, while, in the lower classes, a number of small, moist fists closed still more tightly over the pieces of silver which had been wrapped in paper and pressed carefully into their palms.

The teachers drew chairs and stools to their respective desks and sat down. Each produced a foolscap sheet on which were recorded the names of those of his class who had contributed to the purse for the retiring Head, Mr Megahey.

No commendation seemed due to the donor of threepence. A sixpence was held up between the thumb and forefinger of the receiving teacher and displayed before the class, while the name of the boy who had presented it was repeated some half a dozen times. Still more ado was made of the bestower of a shilling. In addition to being patted on the shoulder and beamed on by his teacher, and basking in the envy of his class, he was sent up to be thanked by the acting Head who shook his hand heartily and showed the gleaming gold of his teeth, and who, with a grave gesture, bestowed upon him the fag-end of a stick of chalk with the injunction that it be not used about the school.

The receipt of the contributions was over, and the last boy had returned to his seat. On the platform the acting Head cleared his throat for attention and said:

'Those who have contributed to our retiring Head's purse will now sit. Those who have *not* will remain standing.'

When the scuffling tumult of a school of boys taking their seats had subsided, here and there about the schoolroom a scattered few stood with downcast eyes.

The acting Head was a squat jug of a man, fierce-eyed and unsmiling. He now sauntered along the edge of his platform and fixed, one after the other, each of the standing boys with a look of complete scorn. Then, mopping his brow, he ordered those who had brought no gifts to come up and mount the platform where the dozen of them were lined up.

Taking a stick of chalk he scrawled an X upon the forehead of each boy, to the huge delight of the rest of the school. When he had imprinted this symbol of shame upon the brow of each unhappy child, he

9

turned to the laughing school, and holding his hand up to check the gusts of merriment, said:

'Look! They bear the symbol of ingratitude!'

The cruel laughter went up to the rafters. The schoolmaster permitted it free swell for a few moments before raising his hand once more.

'Ingratitude,' he went on, 'ingratitude, more strong than human hand . . . Come, Clement. You're in the fourth. Step forward and let's hear Mark Antony on ingratitude. Surely our old Head would expire if he knew that in his school he harboured so many thankless Brutuses. Come, Clement, let us hear you recite the piece, and well.'

Clement stepped forward, shabby and barefoot, and with eyes downcast, began to recite the passage in a choked, monotonous tone. Now and again the schoolmaster threatened him with his rod, exhorting him to speak up. The boy would then raise his voice and quicken his words under the threat of the lash, but soon his voice sank back and the recitation resumed its muttered vein.

At last, however, the passage was finished. The acting Headmaster then spent some minutes more making the hapless boys the laughing-stock of their schoolfriends. Only when he thought the school on the verge of becoming unmanageable did he dismiss the tormented boys with the words:

'Now go to your places. But bear in mind, every morning, until you show some appreciation for your resigning Headmaster, you shall come up here and stand in shame before the whole school.'

It was dusk, and the Dovecots were taking their one substantial meal of the day.

No one could think, looking at their home, that

threepenny pieces, or even halfpennies, were to be had there for the asking.

The house was a poor, wretched coop of a room, through the black, water-stained shingles of which you could count a dozen blue glimpses of the sky. The walls of the shack were papered with old newspapers and magazines, discoloured with age and stained and spotted from roof to floor, torn in a score of places, to reveal the rotting, worm-eaten boards beneath. The small room was divided by a threadbare cotton screen depicting seagulls soaring up from a sea of faded blue. In the midst of this drab poverty the free, soaring seagulls, and the once gay pictures of the magazine pages were an unkind comment.

The Dovecots were a family of four: Dave and his wife Maud, Clement and his older sister Evelina.

*diff. social class.*

Clement sat on the sanded floor of the poor sitting-room, his plate of rice between his legs; Evelina lolled over the one battered, depreciated mahogany table, picking at the coarse food with an adolescent discontent; Dave Dovecot, a grizzled, gangling labourer, held his plate in his left hand, while with his right he plied his mouth from a peeling metal spoon; at the propped-open window of the room sat Mrs Dovecot, a long thread of a woman whose bones want had picked like an eagle. Her plate was resting on her lap, and she scraped and pecked and foraged her food like a scratching hen, while she took stock of the passers-by.

When Clement had finished, he took up his empty plate and, getting to his feet, went and stowed it away in the dark box of a kitchen. Returning, he slumped down beside his mother's chair and rested his head against her bony thigh. *poor family ⇒ cannot afford bribes*

*sense of injustice in readers.*

11

After a time he said:

'Ma, I could have the threepence I's been asking for Mr Megahey?'

'Hmn. Wa' threepence boy? Why in de name of de Lord must poor starving people got to find threepences for Jim Megahey what's got his belly sitting so pretty wi' fat?' parried Mrs Dovecot, though she knew well enough.

'I's told you and told you and told you, Ma. He's resigning and we've all got to take threepence to give him,' explained Clement patiently once more.

'Hmn. Threepence is a lot o' money for us poor folk. Hmn. Go ax your father. See what *he* says.' Clement got to his feet reluctantly and moved slowly over to where his father was sitting, for he knew from experience that, in parting with money, his father was a far harder nut to crack than his mother.

Dave Dovecot utilised the approach of his son by extending his empty plate. Clement took the plate to the kitchen. Then he turned once more to tackle his father.

'Can I have a threepence, Papa?' he shouted in his father's ear, for the old man was pretty nigh stone deaf.

'Eh-eh! What's that about a fence, Clement?'

This time Clement put his mouth completely into his father's ear and shouted until his dark face grew darker.

'Eh-eh! Don't shout at me,' was all he got for his pains. 'Don't you deafen me. What's that the young varmint says, Maud?'

Mrs Dovecot came over, and got him to understand after two or three attempts.

'Three pence, Maudie,' he cackled, 'three pence! Did yo' hear thet, Maud? Did yo' ever hear the like? I'll bet you ain't never did. Three pence! The lad'll have money what I's got to sweat blood for, just to gi to thet

Megahey what's got his bread so well buttered off 'pon both sides not to mention the middle. Three pence! Ha ha! . . . oh Maudie . . .' And he broke down once more in helpless laughter. Clement went out and sat under the breadfruit tree that grew before the door, resting his back against the trunk.

Evelina came to him there when the dusk was thick and sat beside him.

There was a close bond of understanding and companionship between these two. Clement leaned against her so that he could feel the cheering warmth of her arms, warm as the still warm ground beneath him. Biting his nails he told her of his morning's shame.

She listened as attentively as a mother, and as she listened, she put her hand around his neck and drew his head gently down upon her young bosom.

When he had finished talking she put her lips down to his harsh curls, and thought for a long time. Then she said, with a little sigh:

'I know what we'll do, Clemmie. 'Member how 'fore I was took from school we big girls used to go out singing at Christmas? Well, we'll play waits. Only tonight there'll be only you and me.'

Clement raised his head and gazed into her face in the starlight.

'Oh, Eve,' he said, 'but it ain't anyways near Christmas.'

'Never you mind,' she said. 'There's still some who'll give us a penny or two. You wait. I'll get our hats and then we'll be off.'

She got to her feet and slipped quickly into the house. She returned in a few moments carrying his cap in her hand, her own hat of straw on her head. She settled his cap, then produced a comb.

'When we come to the shop we'll ask for a piece of bread paper,' she said, 'then you'll play the sax while I sing.'

They roamed far that night. Evelina's voice rose clear and true to the accompaniment of the paper and comb, long after the moon came up and laid white hands upon the countryside.

At last Evelina said, jingling the coins which they had earned in the pockets of her dress:

'Let's make this our last and call it a day.'

The house with which they proposed to round off their tour had a pretentious front of red brick. The greater part of the house was in darkness, but from the street the two children could see a couple sitting in the open veranda.

Bravely, Evelina unlatched the street gate and led the way up the steps to the veranda.

'Good night,' she greeted the pair in the shadows. 'We would like to sing for you.'

The woman chuckled softly and Evelina could see the white gleam of the man's teeth when he said, 'Sure.'

The children rendered their song. When they had finished the man got to his feet and approached them, delving in his pocket.

'Thanks for your singing,' he said kindly. 'It was very nice. May, give us some light for a moment.'

The woman got from her chair and, leaning through a window, pressed a light switch.

And as the light flooded the veranda little Clement was turned to stone, for the tall, greying man foraging the handful of coins was the retiring Headmaster, Mr Megahey.

Clement's scrambled retreat after Evelina had made her little curtsy was perhaps unnecessary, since Mr

14

Megahey had his glasses off and he didn't seem to recognise him.

Out in the road, Evelina let out the laughter that had been welling inside her.

'Just think how we never thought of where your old Head might've moved to after he left the Schoolmaster's house,' she laughed. 'But he's gi'n us our biggest taking for the night, anyway. He's gi'n us sixpence.'

They counted their takings in the middle of the white road in the moonlight. When they had finished, Evelina poured the coins back into her pocket and said:

'Now I going tell you how we'll fix that brute, Mr Chase.'

On the following morning the acting Head, Mr Chase, kept his word. Immediately after prayers the boys who had brought no silver were lined up across the platform. They were but eight of them this morning. Two had somehow managed their threepenny pieces, while two or three others had absented themselves. Clement counted the line of boys as he took his place among them.

As Mr Chase eyed their bowed heads in enjoyment, Clement stepped forward, the eight pieces of silver upon his extended palm.

'There are eight,' he told the gaping schoolmaster. 'One for *each* of us.'

His voice struck through the silent school, clear and thrilling as a star's light.

*- quite a simple story*

# Focus on character

*- cha. are nameless ⇒ symbols? signs?*

# Crime and Punishment

*title symbolic, linked to rest of story*
*title chosen deliberately to mislead us?*

**by R. K. Narayan**

*link to title as teacher gives punishment + student gives crime.*

'What is sixteen and three multiplied?' asked the teacher. The boy blinked. The teacher persisted, and the boy promptly answered: 'Twenty-four,' with, as it seemed to the teacher, a wicked smile on his lips. The boy evidently was trying to fool him and was being contrary on purpose. He had corrected this error repeatedly, and now the boy persisted in saying twenty-four. How could this fellow be made to obtain fifty in the class test and go up by double-promotion to the first form, as his parents fondly hoped? At the mention of 'twenty-four' the teacher felt his blood rushing to his head. He controlled himself, and asked again: 'How much?' as a last chance. When the boy obstinately said the same, he felt as if his finger were releasing the trigger: he reached across the table, and delivered a wholesome slap on the youngster's cheek. The boy gazed at him for a moment and then burst into tears. The teacher now regained his normal vision, felt appalled by his own action, and begged frantically: 'Don't cry, little fellow, you mustn't . . .'

'I will tell them,' sobbed the boy. 'Oh, no, no, no,' appealed the teacher. He looked about cautiously. Fortunately this nursery was at a little

*— character quite patient already.*

*crime by teacher + gets punished by child.*

*Feel sorry for boy.*

*Stunned, shocked, in pain, flabbergasted — feelings for teacher*

*shows how power can be easily lost by a moment in the store, boy gains authority, upper hand in impulse*

*— humour comic effect*

*tea. → impulsive, subservient, coward, servile, → weak-willed, pathetic*

16

distance from the main building.

'I'll tell my mother,' said the boy.

According to the parents, the boy was a little angel, all dimples, smiles, and sweetness – only wings lacking. He was their only child, they had abundant affection and ample money. They built a nursery, bought him expensive toys, fitted up miniature furniture sets, gave him a small pedal motor car to go about in all over the garden. They filled up his cupboard with all kinds of sweets and biscuits, and left it to his good sense to devour them moderately. They believed a great deal in leaving things that way.

'You must never set up any sort of contrariness or repression in the child's mind,' declared the parents. 'You'll damage him for life. It no doubt requires a lot of discipline on our part, but it is worth it,' they declared, primly. 'We shall be bringing up a healthy citizen.'

'Yes, yes,' the teacher agreed outwardly, feeling more and more convinced every day that what the little fellow needed to make him a normal citizen was not cajoling – but an anna's worth of cane, for which he was prepared to advance the outlay. For the teacher it was a life of utter travail – the only relieving feature in the whole business was the thirty rupees they paid him on every first day. It took him in all three hours every evening – of which the first half an hour he had to listen to the child-psychology theories of the parents. The father had written a thesis on infant psychology for his M.A., and the lady had studied a great deal of it for her B.A. They lectured to him every day on their theories, and he got more and more the feeling that they wanted him to deal with the boy as if he were made of thin glass. He had to pretend that he agreed with them, while his own private view was that he was in charge of a little gorilla.

Now the teacher did not know how to quieten the boy, who kept sobbing. He felt desperate. He told the youngster, 'You must not cry for these trifling matters, you must be like a soldier . . .' —sound subservient, cowardly

'A soldier will shoot with a gun if he is hit,' said the boy in reply. The teacher treated it as a joke and laughed artificially. The boy caught the infection and laughed, too. This eased the situation somewhat. 'Go and wash your face,' suggested the teacher – a fine blue porcelain closet was attached to the nursery. The boy disobeyed and commanded: 'Close the lessons today.' The teacher was aghast. 'No, no,' he cried.

'Then I will go and tell my mother,' threatened the boy. He pushed the chair back and got up. The teacher rushed up to him and held him down. 'My dear fellow, I'm to be here for another hour.' The boy said: 'All right, watch me put the engine on its rails.' —reversal of roles

boy behaving like a teacher

'If your father comes in . . .' said the teacher.

'Tell him it is an engine lesson,' said the boy, and he smiled maliciously. He went over to his cupboard, opened it, took out his train set, and started assembling the track. He wound the engine and put it down, and it went round and round. 'You are the station master,' proclaimed the boy. 'No, no,' cried the teacher. 'You have your tests the day after tomorrow.' The boy merely smiled in a superior way and repeated, 'Will you be a station master or not?' repeatedly gives commands

The teacher was annoyed. 'I won't be a station master,' he said defiantly, whereupon the young fellow said: 'Oh, oh, is that what you say?' He gently touched his cheek, and murmured: 'It is paining me here awfully, I must see my mother.' He made a movement towards the door. The teacher watched him with a dull desperation. The boy's cheek was still red. So he said: 'Don't, boy. You want me to be a station master? What shall I have to do?'

The boy directed, 'When the train comes to your station, you must blow the whistle and cry, "Engine Driver, stop the train. There are a lot of people today who have bought tickets."'

The teacher hunched up in a corner and obeyed. He grew tired of the position and the game in thirty minutes, and got up, much to the displeasure of his pupil. Luckily for him the engine also suddenly refused to move. The boy handed it to him, as he went back to his seat, and said: 'Repair it, sir.' He turned it about in his hand and said: 'I can't. I know nothing about it.'

'It must go,' said the boy firmly. The teacher felt desperate. He was absolutely non-mechanical. He could not turn the simplest screw if it was to save his life. The boy stamped his foot impatiently and waited like a tyrant. The teacher put it away definitely with: 'I can't and I won't.' The boy immediately switched on to another demand. 'Tell me a story . . .'

'You haven't done a sum. It is eight-thirty.'

'I don't care for sums,' said the boy. 'Tell me a story.'

'No . . .'

The boy called, 'Appa! Appa!'

'Why are you shouting like that for your father?'

'I have something to tell him, something important . . .'

The teacher was obliged to begin the story of a bison and a tiger, and then he passed on to 'Ali Baba and the Forty Thieves' and 'Aladdin's Lamp'. The boy listened, rapt, and ordered: 'I want to hear the story of the bison again. It is good . . .' The teacher was short of breath. He had done six hours of teaching at school during the day. 'Tomorrow. I've lost all my breath . . .'

'Oh! All right. I'll go and tell . . .' exclaimed the boy; he got up and started running all of a sudden towards

19

the house, and the teacher started after him. The boy
was too fast for him, and wheeled about madly, and
made the teacher run round the garden thrice. The
teacher looked beaten. The boy took pity on him and
stopped near the rose bush. But the moment he went
up and tried to put his hand on him, the boy darted
through and ran off. It was a hopeless pursuit; the boy
enjoyed it immensely, laughing fiendishly. The
teacher's face was flushed and he gasped uncomfor-
tably. He felt a darkness swelling up around him. He
sank down on the portico step.

At this moment Father and Mother emerged from
the house. 'What is the matter?' The teacher struggled
up to his feet awkwardly. He was still panting badly and
could not talk. He had already made up his mind that
he would confess and take the consequence, rather
than stand the blackmail by this boy. It seemed less
forbidding to throw himself at the mercy of the elders.
They looked inquiringly at the boy and asked: 'Why
have you been running in the garden at this hour?'
The boy looked mischievously at the teacher. The
teacher cleared his throat and said: 'I will explain . . .'
He was trying to find the words for his sentence. The
father asked: 'How's he preparing for his test in
arithmetic . . .?' On hearing the word 'test' the boy's
face fell; he unobtrusively slunk behind his parents and
by look and gestures appealed to the teacher not to
betray him. He looked so pathetic and desperate that
the teacher replied: 'Only please let him mug up the
16th table a little more . . . He is all right. He will pull
through.' The boy looked relieved. The teacher saw his
grateful face, felt confident that the boy would not give
him up now, and said: 'Good night, sir; we finished our
lessons early, and I was just playing about with the child
. . . something to keep up his spirits, you know.'

# Warrior Woman

**by Nancy Chong**

*[handwritten annotations: -no plot -no climax -1st person narrative; first person narrative -person writing is a voice -remembering her as a child.]*

In 1960, the city of Toronto tore down blocks of buildings in old Chinatown to make way for the new City Hall at Queen and Bay. The Golden Dragon Restaurant on Dundas Street, once owned by my father, escaped destruction. The old hotel, once owned by my father's uncle, crumbled under the wrecker's ball. My mother took me to see a movie in old Chinatown, before the city tore down the old movie theatre.

*[handwritten margin notes: of change; cousin; idea of; replaced; new; setting; economic background of family; migrants; too.]*

My mother rarely dressed up to go out. I watched her get ready to go to the movie. She stood in the kitchen and looked into the mirror of the small wooden cabinet that held our toothbrushes. On the counter below, she placed a small pot of rouge, a red lipstick, a compact of face powder and a small, silky powder puff. My mother leaned closer to the mirror and examined her eyes. She ran her fingertips slowly over her eyebrows.

*[handwritten margin notes: So what? Emphasizes that she rarely does it off time; ticks to; stain; adding on; this makeup.]*

My mother pulled open the cabinet drawer and took out a spool of thread. She unwound a length of thread and doubled it, attached one end of the thread to the cabinet and held the doubled end in one hand, winding the loose end of the thread around the fingers of her other hand. Holding the doubled thread against her eyebrows and twirling it between her fingers, she caught a stray hair between the twisted threads. With a quick tug, my mother plucked the offending hair from

*[handwritten margin note: how she retained her culture or cu roots.]*

21

her eyebrows. She shaped each eyebrow into a thin graceful arch.

Next, my mother smeared a dab of rouge on her cheeks and rubbed it into her skin until her cheeks glowed. She patted the powder puff on her cheeks and around her nose. Then she carefully outlined her lips with the tip of the red lipstick. She stopped to examine her lips. Satisfied, she completed painting her lips with the red lipstick. For the final touch, she darkened her eyebrows with the charred tip of a burnt wooden match.

My mother buttoned the back of my dress and tied the bow behind me. I tugged at my white socks and straightened the strap on my shiny black patent shoes. Dressed and ready, I impatiently watched my mother fasten the clasp on her gold-and-jade bracelet and then clip her gold-and-jade earrings to her ears. She straightened her dress, pushed aside the curtain hanging over her bedroom door and stepped into the hall. With her handbag hanging on her bent arm, she walked out of the front door. I followed.

'Hurry!' my mother said. 'Hong's wife is waiting.' We were going to the movies with Cousin Hong's wife. I had never gone to the movies before. My mother walked quickly down Phoebe Street, her high heels clicking on the concrete sidewalk. I walked beside her and stepped over the cracks in the concrete. Step on a crack and break your mother's back.

My cousin and his family lived on McCaul Street, about a fifteen-minute walk from our house. Cousin Hong drank. My sister E told me how one night Hong's wife hid behind a door with a broomstick, waiting to attack him when he came home drunk. Hong's wife had a name, but we called her Hong's Wife because that was her position in our family.

22

We walked up Huron Street, across Sullivan Street and turned the corner at Beverley Street. We walked past the art gallery toward McCaul, past the used clothing store and the store that sold live chickens and around the corner to my cousin's house.

'Coming to the movie?' Hong's Wife asked. She did not wait for me to answer. She turned to my mother. I did not listen to their gossip. I thought only of the movie. From McCaul, my mother, Hong's wife and I walked to old Chinatown, near the intersection of Dundas and Elizabeth.

We walked into the dimly lit theatre, its empty seats lined in rows before us. I followed my mother to the front row. She held the seat down for me. I sat on the red plush seat, sinking into the upholstery, my feet dangling, and stared up at the stage, draped with heavy red curtains.

The theatre darkened while the heavy red curtains slowly rose to reveal a large blank white screen. I waited for the movie to start.

Chinese characters, bright white against the brilliant colours, flashed across the screen. The strains of stringed music, unfamiliar, whining and plaintive, filled the air.

Warrior Woman leapt on the screen. Warrior Woman floated through the air like a cloud, white silk flowing around her like wispy trails of smoke. Red lips, glowing cheeks, painted eyes and soaring eyebrows emphasized her powdered white face. She shouted at her opponent. I could not understand what she said. Warrior Woman stood, her head tilted, hand on her sword, challenging her enemy with her stance. Chinese subtitles lined the bottom of the screen for anyone who could not understand the Chinese dialect spoken by the actors.

23

losing Chinese roots/culture

I could not read the subtitles, but it did not matter. I understood Warrior Woman. She defeated all who challenged her. Men shouted as they charged Warrior Woman, but she fearlessly fought them off. I turned my head and looked at my mother to see if she was watching Warrior Woman. My mother's head tilted slightly to one side, her eyes closed while she slept. I turned back to the screen and watched Warrior Woman battle another foe.

The movie ended when Warrior Woman defeated all her enemies. Warrior Woman stood, victorious in battle, feet astride the rocky crest of a hill, one hand on her hip, the other arm raised with sword in hand, catching the sunlight, a blinding glare glancing off its deadly blade. Then rows of Chinese characters rolled up the screen, concealing Warrior Woman's defiant gaze.

As we walked up the aisle to the exit, I looked back. The heavy red curtains slowly lowered to cover the screen, sealing off Warrior Woman's world.

We walked out into the street, shielding our eyes from the bright sunlight. We walked across a large empty lot bounded on the south by Queen Street and on the east by Bay Street. We walked toward Queen Street, TTC streetcars visible in the distance. My mother held my hand as we stepped on the bits of stone and rubble from recently demolished buildings. She gossiped with Hong's Wife and paid little attention to me.

Walking hand-in-hand with my mother felt natural. I imagined how we looked. I thought about the eight-by-ten photographs of my two American cousins who lived in Chicago. We had photographs of the sisters, dressed in matching outfits, smiling for the camera, walking

24

_opp. oriental_

along the street, reaching up to hold their mother's white-gloved hands. _Symbolise acceptance of e occidental values, lifestyle_

The perfect picture faded. My mother never took me to see a movie again. My mother never walked hand in hand with me again. Whenever I looked at the family photo album, I could not avoid the last pages, dominated by the eight-by-ten photographs of my American cousins. They looked like part of the perfect American family. The perfection captured in their photographs seemed a distant dream to me. _never_ _another occasion_

_feel apart fr e perfect Picture of an Ame. family._

_Was. women on film ⇒ alien to writer_
_world_
_— somethg cannot understand_
_— poignant, touching, sad ending_
_— wr ⇒ state of transi^n_
_— not quite fully Americanised_
_— ⊾ Yet losing Q._

_— Simple, straightforward story trying to capture e writer's memory ⇒ going to e movie with Mum._

# The Easter Hat

**by Nancy Chong**

I went to Sunday school with my sisters and brothers at the Chinese United Church on Chestnut Street until, at the age of ten, I refused to go. For years, Sundays meant Sunday school and cold wet laundry. Mr Lee, the minister, drove us to church every Sunday in his station wagon. My mother stayed home to do the weekly wash in a wringer washer that she dragged over to the sink in the kitchen. She attended church services infrequently except for special occasions like Christmas and Easter. My sister E and I sang in the church choir after Sunday school finished. The choir practised the hymns before the service started and had cake and cookies after the church service finished.

E and I usually came home to find baskets of cold wet laundry, squeezed flat by the rollers of the wringer washer, waiting for us to hang out on the clotheslines stretched across the backyard. In the winter, we hung the laundry on clotheslines stretched across the kitchen and in the cold, dark cellar.

Palm Sunday signalled the coming of Easter. On Palm Sunday the older kids at Sunday school got long stalks of dry, yellow grass to take home. I knew that the following Sunday we would each get an Easter basket with chocolate and candy eggs tucked into a nest of crumpled strips of green paper.

Palm Sunday also signalled my mother's annual shopping trip to Eaton's for an Easter hat. I went on one of those shopping trips with her. We took the streetcar on Queen Street from Spadina to the Eaton's store across from the City Hall at Queen and Bay. My mother usually shopped at the cheaper Eaton's Annex on Albert Street, but this time we went through the wood-and-glass revolving doors into the main store on Queen Street.

I walked through the store aisles with my mother, staring at the dark wood-and-glass display cases filled with gloves, scarves, stockings, perfumes. I looked up and saw a single plaster leg wearing a nylon stocking. The leg stood by itself on top of a display case. Hands wearing white gloves reached up from the top of another display case.

We stopped in front of the wood-and-glass case displaying rows of hats, clusters of flowers, yellow, pink and white, surrounded by lace. My mother pointed at a pink hat.

'Do you want to see that?' asked a saleswoman.

'How much?' my mother asked. She fingered the lace flowers on the pink hat.

'Do you want to try it on?' The saleswoman smiled and held out the hat. She turned the mirror to face my mother. My mother picked up the hat and placed it gently on top of her head. The saleswoman leaned over and carefully stuck a pearl-tipped hatpin into the hat, securing the cluster of lace flowers to my mother's hair. My mother turned her head from side to side, looking in the mirror to check her profile.

—'Too much money,' my mother said to the saleswoman. My mother waited for a reply. The saleswoman shook her head.

—'Five dollar off?' my mother asked. The saleswoman held out her hands for the hat.

27

'I'm afraid I can't do that.' The saleswoman frowned.

'Two dollar off?' my mother asked again. The saleswoman opened the wood-and-glass case to return the hat to the display. 'How much?' My mother sighed as she opened her purse. She counted out her money. The saleswoman took the pink hat and wrapped it in layers of tissue and carefully placed it in an Eaton's hat box. She covered the hat with more tissue and then dropped the lid on the hat box. Lifting the hat box by the carrying strap, the saleswoman handed it to my mother. My mother took the hat box, conscious of its fine contents.

At home, my mother put the Eaton's hat box away. She placed it carefully on the mantel over the cemented-in fireplace in her bedroom. When she wasn't looking, I crept into the bedroom to look at the hat. I climbed up on a chair and lifted the lid on the hat box. I pushed aside layers of tissue to reveal the precious hat. In the darkness of the room, the hat seemed even more delicate. I put the hat back into the box, careful not to make too much noise with the crinkling tissue.

My mother took the hat out of the hat box on Easter Sunday, unpacking it from the layers of tissue. She put the hat on her head, securing it with the pearl-tipped hatpin, just as the saleswoman at Eaton's had. She attended Easter services at the Chinese United Church with the Easter hat from Eaton's on her head. She sat in the church pew among rows of many more fine Easter hats.

After my mother got home from church, she returned the hat to the Eaton's hat box. She replaced the layers of tissue and dropped the lid into place. Lifting the hat box by the carrying strap, she put it back on the mantel over the fireplace in her bedroom.

The next shopping day, my mother dressed to go out. She took the Eaton's hat box down from the mantel and checked her purse for the sales slip. She picked up the hat box by the carrying strap along with her purse.

My mother went back to the Eaton's store on Queen Street. Eaton's guaranteed 'Goods Satisfactory Or Money Refunded' on purchases returned with a sales slip within seven days.

My mother returned the hat and got her money back, just as she did every Easter.

*[Handwritten annotations:]*

- tone of disgust, disapproval?
- like W.W?
- amused & admiration.
- just telling a story, plain.
- resignation, exasperation
- may look back at time ⇒ poetic exasperation now: amused, admiration.
needs challenges to inject meaning into her mundane, ordinary, routine life.
- in struggle to assimilate ⇒ like WW which fight within herself. foreign culture ⇒ celebrates Easter by buying a hat.
- a chance to dress up.

To a 2nd generation migrant, a lot of cultural roots are adulterated & eroded ∴ what remains is she's more comfortable speaking Eng. but not totally Ame. like cousins.
- Strange intercultural mix.

# Focus on setting

## Kill to Eat

**by Oodgeroo Nunukul**

My father worked for the Government, as ganger of an Aboriginal workforce which helped to build roads, load and unload the supply ships, and carry out all the menial tasks around the island. For this work he received a small wage and rations to feed his seven children. (I was the third-eldest daughter.) We hated the white man's rations – besides, they were so meagre that even a bandicoot would have had difficulty in existing on them. They used to include meat, rice, sago, tapioca, and on special occasions, such as the Queen's Birthday festival, one plum pudding.

Of course, we never depended upon the rations to keep ourselves alive. Dad taught us how to catch our food Aboriginal-style, using discarded materials from the white man's rubbish dumps. We each had our own sling-shots to bring down the blueys and greenies – the parrots and lorikeets that haunted the flowering gums. And he showed us how to make bandicoot traps; a wooden box, a bit of wire, a lever on top and a piece of burnt toast were all that was needed. Bandicoots cannot resist burnt toast. We would set our traps at dusk, and always next day there was a trapped bandicoot to take proudly home for Mother to roast. Dad also showed us how to flatten a square piece of tin and sharpen it. This was very valuable for slicing through the shallow waters; many a mullet met its doom from the accurate aim of one of my brothers wielding the sharpened tin. Dad made long iron crab hooks, too, and we each had a hand fishing-line of our own.

One rule he told us we must strictly obey. When we went hunting, we must understand that our weapons were to be used only for the gathering of food. We must never use them for the sake of killing. This is in fact one of the strictest laws of the Aborigine, and no excuse is accepted for abusing it.

One day we five older children, two boys and three girls, decided to follow the noise of the blueys and greenies screeching from the flowering gums. We armed ourselves with our sling-shots and made our way towards the trees.

My sisters and I always shot at our quarry from the ground. The boys would climb on to the branches of the gum-trees, stand quite still, and pick out the choicest and healthiest birds in the flock. My elder brother was by far the best shot of all of us. He was always boasting about it, too. But never in front of our mother and father, because he would have been punished for his vanity. He only boasted in front of us, knowing that we wouldn't complain about him to our parents.

The boys ordered us to take up our positions under the trees as quietly as possible. 'Don't make so much noise!' they told us. In spite of the disgust we felt for our boastful brother, we always let him start the shooting. He was a dead shot, and we all knew it. Now we watched as he drew a bead on the large bluey straight across from him. The bird seemed intent on its honey-gathering from the gum-tree. We held our

31

breath and our brother fired.

Suddenly there was a screeching from the birds and away they flew, leaving my brother as astonished as we were ourselves. He had been so close to his victim that it seemed impossible he should have missed . . . but he had. We looked at him, and his face of blank disbelief was just too much for us. We roared with laughter. My other brother jumped to the ground and rolled over and over, laughing his head off. But the more we laughed, the angrier my elder brother became.

Then, seeming to join in the fun, a kookaburra in a nearby tree started his raucous chuckle, which rose to full pitch just as though he, too, saw the joke.

In anger my elder brother brought up his sling-shot and fired blindly at the sound. 'Laugh at me, would you!' he called out. He hadn't even taken time to aim.

Our laughter was cut short by the fall of the kookaburra to the ground. My brother, horrified, his anger gone, climbed down and we gathered silently around the stricken bird. That wild aim had broken the bird's wing beyond repair. We looked at each other in frightened silence, knowing full well what we had done. We had broken that strict rule of the Aboriginal law. We had killed for the sake of killing – and we had destroyed a bird we were forbidden to destroy. The Aborigine does not eat the kookaburra. His merry laughter is allowed to go unchecked, for he brings happiness to the tribes. We call him our brother and friend.

We did not see our father coming towards us. He must have been looking for firewood. When he came upon us, we parted to allow him to see what had happened. He checked his anger by remaining silent and picking up a fallen branch. Mercifully he put the stricken bird out of its misery. Then he ordered us home.

On the way back we talked with awesome foreboding

32

of the punishment we knew would come. I wished our father would beat us, but we all knew it would not be a quick punishment. Besides, Dad never beat us. No, we knew the punishment would be carefully weighed to fit the crime. When we got home, our mother was told to give us our meal. Nothing was said of the dead kookaburra, but we knew Dad would broach the subject after we had eaten. None of us felt hungry, and our mother only played with her food. We knew that Dad had decided upon the punishment, and that Mother had agreed to it, even if she felt unhappy about it.

It was our mother who ordered us to bring into the backyard our bandicoot traps, our sling-shots, and every other weapon we had. We had to place them in a heap in the yard, while our father carefully checked every item. Our big black dog stood with us. He always did that when there was trouble in the family. Although he could not possibly understand the ways of human beings, he could nevertheless interpret an atmosphere of trouble when it came.

Father spoke for the first time since we had killed the kookaburra. He asked for no excuses for what we had done, and we did not offer any. We must all take the blame. That is the way of the Aborigine. Since we had killed for the sake of killing, the punishment was that for three months we should not hunt or use our weapons. For three months we would eat only the white man's hated rations.

During those three months our stomachs growled, and our puzzled dog would question with his eyes and wagging tail why we sat around wasting our time when there was hunting to be done.

It happened a long time ago. Yet in my dreams, the sad, suffering eyes of the kookaburra, our brother and friend, still haunt me.

33

# What Do You Do in Winter?

## by Marion Strachan

At the start of every summer the small town resolutely put on powder and lipstick, dressed itself up and set out to please the strangers it attracted. English strangers. 'Their money,' said Mam as she fried their breakfast bacon and eggs in plenty of lard, 'is as good as anyone else's.' Overnight, shops and cafés opened up and Bed and Breakfast signs appeared in every other parlour window. The chapels tried to make themselves inconspicuous and the church put on an English service for the annual encampment of Boys Brigade which marched through the town with its trumpets blaring. Every year, old Will Thomas the Post stood on his front step and shouted: 'Tell Joshua to mind those castle walls, boys. You're not in Jericho now!' My sister and her friends sat on the wall outside our house swinging their precocious legs, wolf-whistling at the smooth-cheeked boy scouts and making them blush as they walked downhill to the beach from the farm where they camped.

The summer I was almost fourteen Mam found work for me in the town's fanciest fancy-goods store. Six days a week, nine o'clock until six – there was still plenty of time to serve the strangers their breakfast before running to work with my friend Deilwen. The store's owners were a brother and sister who went away to England in winter and banned us from speaking Welsh in the shop. 'It's very rude,' they said, 'to speak Welsh

34

when you know we can't understand you.' Deilwen and I were brought up to be polite girls and we giggled our way through stilted English conversations with each other all summer. When one of the strangers I was serving with a seashell-covered box said, 'This is a lovely place for a holiday, but what do you do in winter?', neither of us could answer him because we didn't know the English words for the way the town behaved in winter.

As soon as the last stranger left at the end of summer, the town scrubbed off its make-up, stopped acting and returned to reality. Welsh was its language all week and the language of Heaven on Sundays. My sister and I slept in our own beds again and Mam burnt the breakfast porridge before we went to school.

That winter of my fourteenth birthday, I decided, would be the winter when I won back the first place in the recitation contest at our chapel's Eisteddfod. I had been placed second ever since Mr Morgan, our French teacher at school, had taken over the judging of the competition. Meinir Owen always won. She was an orphan, a thin, mournful child, and Mr Morgan's soft heart could not abandon her the way her parents had. I couldn't compete. But that winter a way of making our situations a little more evenly matched occurred to me. I thought a dying mother would attract Mr Morgan's sympathy as much as a dead one. Mam had become quite fat over the summer. She said it was the smell of the breakfast lard, and I told Mr Morgan, with suitably damp eyes and my fingers crossed, that Mam was dying slowly of a mysterious disease which would make her fatter and fatter until the End came. 'You poor child,' said Mr Morgan, 'oh, you poor child.'

Soon after that my form tutor, Miss Roberts, took me aside and said I could tell her everything, absolutely

35

everything. Miss Roberts attended the services in our chapel because she was sweet on the man who raised the singing, and every Sunday after that I could see her watching Mam sorrowfully as we walked in. Mam noticed the expression but thought she was lovesick. I heard her say so to Tada. 'I'm telling you, Gwynfor,' she said, 'that Heulwen Roberts will be married to poor Gruffydd Pugh before the Bed and Breakfast signs are up next summer.'

Tada wasn't interested, but Mam was right. Every year, just before Christmas, the adults in our chapel put on a play in the Memorial Hall. The play that winter had a scene where Gruffydd Pugh and Miss Roberts had to pretend to kiss passionately, but they didn't pretend and there were whistles and cat-calls and foot stampings from the rowdier element in the audience to show that the lack of pretence had been noticed. After that they had to get married.

During the weeks before Christmas, while Miss Roberts and Gruffydd Pugh practised kissing, the rest of the town prepared for the Eisteddfod. Once the programmes were published and I knew which poem I had to recite, Mam sent me to Mrs Jones the Graves every Saturday morning for tuition. Mrs Jones was what Mam called 'a real lady' though she wasn't English. She had married beneath her to Sulwyn Jones the Graves who, not long after their marriage, had lost both his legs in a terrible accident involving gelignite when he was digging a new grave in a particularly rocky part of the town cemetery. Rumour said that he had taken some alcoholic drink at the time but no one dared suggest this to Mrs Jones whose family had been teetotal and chapel for generations. She looked as if she had stepped out of one of the old photographs my grandfather had hanging in his parlour: no smile on her face, hair pulled tightly back and black dresses Mam said must have belonged to her grandmother. But she was the best teacher of recitation and she took only the best pupils. She always taught Deilwen and me but not Meinir Owen, which hardened my conviction that it was Meinir's status rather than talent which won her the contest. The poem that year was about death and eternity. Mrs Jones the Graves had a walking stick which she held horizontally until Deilwen and I were able to say 'eternity' as straight as the stick with no intonation. It made the word so sombre it sent shivers down our spines. Mrs Jones had a reward for us one Saturday, she had made some toffee. Deilwen and I took a greedy piece each, then, as an acrid taste seeped into our mouths and tightened our jaws, we pushed the lumps into our cheeks and held them there until we could leave the house and run round the corner and spit them out. We agreed that perhaps real ladies were not brought up to make toffee the way our mothers were.

Dwelling on death every Saturday morning with Sulwyn Jones the Graves in the background as a constant reminder of its horrors made me uneasy about the fate I had chosen for Mam. I was perturbed to see that Mam really was growing fatter and fatter, and I wondered if my telling such a lie to Mr Morgan had somehow placed her in the grip of a deadly disease which would kill her just as I had described.

'I know about your Mam,' said Gwyneth Roberts on the way to school one morning. Gwyneth and I disliked one another but had got into the habit of walking to school together because I passed her house on the way there. I disliked Gwyneth's mother, too, who repeatedly told me that I would never have a boyfriend unless I made myself pretty. Gwyneth had several boyfriends, or so she said, much older than us. She was what Mam

-very religious
- yet strong touches on hypocrisy.
           Survival?    reality of life? Rest of growing up?
MARION STRACHAN

called 'well developed', which was very embarrassing in
the showers at school after games; Deilwen and I hoped
fervently that we would never get like that.

'What do you know about my Mam?'

'If you don't know, I'm not going to say.' Gwyneth
often implied that she knew things I didn't, things I felt
uncomfortable about not knowing but wasn't sure I'd
understand if I did know. I wished I hadn't told Mr
Morgan that lie. I couldn't imagine how Gwyneth knew
about Mam dying but I seemed to have made a terrible
thing come true just by saying it.

I needed to tell someone what I had done. The only
person who wouldn't be cross with me was Nain. She
was Tada's mother and Mam said she was a good woman
even though she didn't go to chapel. Something that
happened a long time ago made Nain say that chapel flashback
people were hypocrites. I usually went to see her on
Fridays, but since the end of summer Friday evenings
had been taken up with preparations for the chapel's
nativity play in which I was the narrator. Nain always cut
very, very thin slices of brown bread for me and spread
them with yellow farm butter, then poured my tea into
a cup so fine I was afraid I would take a bite out of it. We
lived in the house next door when I was younger. We
moved to a bigger house with a bathroom so that Mam
could earn money in the summer by taking some
strangers in for bed and breakfast. The bathroom was
cold but it was better than sitting in the tub in front of
the living-room fire in the old house, afraid that Bryn
Hughes the Bread would come whistling through the
door with a large white loaf and a Hovis tucked under
his arm and catch me with no clothes on.

'Now then, little one,' said Nain, 'what a muddle.
Your Mam isn't ill, she's expecting a baby.'

A baby. That was what Gwyneth Roberts knew.

-use of flashback of something. that happened

'When?'

'Christmas Day. Think of that, a Christmas baby.'

'But, Nain, that means that Mr Morgan will know before the Eisteddfod that I lied to him. I won't win.'

'You wouldn't really like to win for the wrong reason, would you?'

'Meinir Owen always does.'

'That's true,' said Nain. 'Well, from what I hear, poor Mr Morgan is a sick man, sick in his mind, takes everything to heart. He lodges with Dic Evans the Undertaker and his wife and yesterday Mrs Evans was telling me he has to go away for a long rest. They'll miss the money just before Christmas.'

I ran all the way home and yelled at the ghost in the churchyard as I passed, 'Mam's having a Christmas baby and Mr Morgan isn't judging the recitation!' and shouted it again as I rushed through the front door. Mam hushed me because she didn't want the neighbours to know yet.

The first prize would be mine. Every Saturday morning with Mrs Jones the Graves my 'eternity' along the stick became straighter and straighter until I could say it in a way which Mrs Jones said would chill the audience to the marrow. Deilwen's 'eternity' wasn't so chilling but she didn't mind because she always won the singing competition. She had a clear, sweet voice which broke your heart. I practised at home after school until Mam said she would be glad when that old Eisteddfod was over and done with.

On Christmas Day Tada woke Mair and me early in the morning and told us we had a new sister. Mair started crying because Mam wouldn't be home for Christmas and we wouldn't have Christmas dinner but Tada said we were going to Nain's house to eat.

'Just think,' he said, 'we won't be able to have

strangers here for bed and breakfast in the summer. Not with a baby in the house. Isn't that a fine thing?'

Mam and Tada brought the baby to the Eisteddfod. Everyone wore their Sunday best and the chapel vestry was filled to its edges. It was too hot because Mrs Williams Chapel House suffered from the cold and always turned the heaters on too high. We all sang 'A pure heart' and then Mr Lloyd the Bank, who was presiding, introduced the judges. The judge who had taken Mr Morgan's place came from miles away and had brought several contestants with her. The craft entries were judged first and Mair won third prize for a tea cosy Mam had made her knit. Then Deilwen sang and there was no sound in the room except for her lovely voice soaring like an angel to Heaven and then everyone clapped until their hands ached and of course she won.

Then it was time for the recitation. One of the visitors was very good but I had been taught by Mrs Jones the Graves. I went on last. I stood on the stage and Mam waved at me. I recited better than I had ever done. 'Eternity' came out every syllable as straight as the stick and the audience gasped and shivered at the bleakness of it in that hot room. Then it was over and the judge gave her decision. Fourth place, Meinir Owen, and quite right too. Deilwen was in third place and gave me a pleased smile. In second place – me. The first prize was won by the visitor. The reason the judge gave for placing me second was that 'eternity' didn't have enough warmth and passion in it. Silence met the judge's speech. She didn't know that she was speaking to an audience who had a surfeit of warmth and passion during their frenetic summer season and had no desire to see it last forever, an audience which luxuriated in the idea of an eternal winter.

# The Steel Windpipe

## by Mikhail Bulgakov

translated from Russian by Michael Glenny

So I was alone, surrounded by November gloom and whirling snow; the house was smothered in it and there was a moaning in the chimneys. I had spent all twenty-four years of my life in a huge city and thought that blizzards only howled in novels. It appeared that they howled in real life. The evenings here are unusually long, and I fell to daydreaming, staring at the reflection on the window of the lamp with its dark green shade. I dreamed of the nearest town, thirty-two miles away. I longed to leave my country clinic and go there. They had electricity, and there were four doctors whom I could consult. At all events it would be less frightening than this place. But there was no chance of running away, and at times I realised that it would be cowardly. It was for precisely this, after all, that I had been studying medicine.

'Yes, but suppose they bring me a woman in labour and there are complications? Or, say, a patient with a strangulated hernia? What shall I do then? Kindly tell me that. Forty-eight days ago I qualified "with distinction", but distinction is one thing and hernia is another. Once I watched a professor operating on a strangulated hernia. He did it, while I sat in the amphitheatre. And I only just managed to survive . . .'

More than once I broke out in a cold sweat down my spine at the thought of hernia. Every evening, as I drank my tea, I would sit in the same attitude: by my

41

left hand lay all the manuals on obstetrical surgery, on top of them the small edition of Döderlein. To my right were ten different illustrated volumes on operative surgery. I groaned, smoked and drank tea without milk.

Once I fell asleep. I remember that night perfectly – it was 29 November, and I was woken by someone banging on the door. Five minutes later I was pulling on my trousers, my eyes glued imploringly to those sacred books on operative surgery. I could hear the creaking of sleigh-runners in the yard – my ears had become unusually sensitive. The case turned out to be, if anything, even more terrifying than a hernia or a transverse foetus. At eleven o'clock that night a little girl was brought to the Muryovo hospital. The nurse said tonelessly to me:

'The little girl's weak, she's dying . . . Would you come over to the hospital, please, doctor . . .'

I remember crossing the yard towards the hospital porch, mesmerised by the flickering light of a kerosene lamp. The lights were on in the surgery, and all my assistants were waiting for me, already dressed in their overalls: the *feldsher* Demyan Lukich, young but very capable, and two experienced midwives, Anna Nikolaevna and Pelagea Ivanovna. Only twenty-four years old, having qualified a mere two months ago, I had been placed in charge of the Muryovo hospital.

The *feldsher* solemnly flung open the door, and the mother came in – or rather she seemed to fly in, slithering on her ice-covered felt boots, unmelted snow still on her shawl. In her arms she carried a bundle, from which came a steady hissing, whistling sound. The mother's face was contorted with noiseless weeping. When she had thrown off her sheepskin coat and shawl and unwrapped the bundle, I saw a little girl of about three years old. For a while the sight of her made me forget operative surgery, my loneliness, the load of useless knowledge acquired at university: it was all completely effaced by the beauty of this baby girl. What can I liken her to? You only see children like that on chocolate boxes – hair curling naturally into big ringlets the colour of ripe rye, enormous dark blue eyes, doll-like cheeks. They used to draw angels like that. But in the depths of her eyes was a strange cloudiness and I recognised it as terror – the child could not breathe. 'She'll be dead in an hour,' I thought with absolute certainty, feeling a sharp twinge of pity for the child.

Her throat was contracting into hollows with each breath, her veins were swollen and her face was turning from pink to a pale lilac. I immediately realised what this colouring meant. I made my first diagnosis, which was not only correct but, more important, was given at the same moment as the midwives' with all their experience: 'The little girl has diphtherial croup. Her throat is already choked with membrane and soon it will be blocked completely.'

'How long has she been ill?' I asked, breaking the tense silence of my assistants. _afraid of surgery, reflec~ of backward knowledge._

'Five days now,' the mother answered, staring hard at me with dry eyes.

'Diphtheria,' I said to the *feldsher* through clenched teeth, and turned to the mother:

'Why have you left it so long?'

At that moment I heard a tearful voice behind me: 'Five days, sir, five days!' — _T. of fear for child._

I turned round and saw that a round-faced old woman had silently come in. 'I wish these old women didn't exist,' I thought to myself. With an aching presentiment of trouble I said:

'Quiet, woman, you're only in the way,' and repeated

to the mother: 'Why have you left it so long? Five days? Hmm?'

Suddenly with an automatic movement the mother handed the little girl to the grandmother and sank to her knees in front of me.

'Give her some medicine,' she said and banged her forehead on the floor. 'I'll kill myself if she dies.'

'Get up at once,' I replied, 'or I won't even talk to you.'

The mother stood up quickly with a rustle of her wide skirt, took the baby from the grandmother and started rocking it. The old woman turned to the doorpost and began praying, while the little girl continued to breathe with a snake-like hiss. The *feldsher* said:

'That's what they're all like. These people!' And he gave a twitch of his moustache.

'Does that mean she's going to die?' the mother asked, staring at me with what looked like black fury.

'Yes, she'll die,' I said quietly and firmly.

The grandmother picked up the hem of her skirt and wiped her eyes. The mother shouted in an ugly voice:

'Give her something! Help her! Give her some medicine!'

I could see what was in store for me and remained firm.

'What medicine can I give her? Go on, you tell me. The little girl is suffocating, her throat is already blocked up. For five days you kept her ten miles away from me. Now what do you want me to do?'

'You're the one who's supposed to know,' the old woman whined by my left shoulder in an affected voice which made me immediately detest her.

'Shut up!' I said to her. I turned to the *feldsher* and ordered the little girl to be taken away. The mother handed her to the midwife and the child started to struggle, evidently trying to cry, but her voice could no longer make itself heard. The mother made a protective move towards her, but we kept her away and I managed to look into the little girl's throat by the light of the pressure-lamp. I had never seen diphtheria before except for mild, forgettable cases. Her throat was full of ragged, pulsating, white substance. The little girl suddenly breathed out and spat in my face, but I was so absorbed that I did not flinch.

'Well now,' I said, astonished at my own calm. 'This is the situation: it's late, and the little girl is dying. Nothing will help her except one thing – an operation.'

I was appalled, wondering why I had said this, but I could not help saying it. The thought flashed through my mind: 'What if she agrees to it?'

'How do you mean?' the mother asked.

'I'll have to cut open her throat near the bottom of her neck and put in a silver pipe so that she can breathe, and then maybe we can save her,' I explained.

The mother looked at me as if I was mad and shielded the little girl from me with her arms, while the old woman started muttering again:

'The idea! Don't you let them cut her open! What – cut her throat?'

'Go away, old woman,' I said to her with hatred. 'Inject the camphor!' I ordered the *feldsher*.

The mother refused to hand over the little girl when she saw the syringe, but we explained to her that there was nothing terrible about it.

'Perhaps that will cure her?' she asked.

'No, it won't cure her at all.'

Then the mother burst into tears.

'Stop it,' I said. I took out my watch, and added: 'I'm giving you five minutes to think it over. If you don't agree in five minutes, I shall refuse to do it.'

45

'I don't agree!' the mother said sharply.

'No, we won't agree to it,' the grandmother put in.

'It's up to you,' I said in a hollow voice, and thought: 'Well, that's that. It makes it easier for me. I've said my piece and given them a chance. Look how dumbfounded the midwives are. They've refused and I'm saved.' No sooner had I thought this than some other being spoke for me in a voice that was not mine:

'Look, have you gone mad? What do you mean by not agreeing? You're condemning the baby to death. You must consent. Have you no pity?'

'No!' the mother shouted once more.

I thought to myself: 'What am I doing? I shall only kill the child.' But I said:

'Come on, come on – you've got to agree! You must! Look, her nails are already turning blue.'

'No, no!'

'All right, take them to the ward. Let them sit there.'

They were led away down the half-lit passage. I could hear the weeping of the women and the hissing of the little girl. The *feldsher* returned almost at once and said:

'They've agreed!'

I felt my blood run cold, but I said in a clear voice:

'Sterilise a scalpel, scissors, hooks and a probe at once.'

A minute later I was running across the yard, through a swirling, blinding snowstorm. I rushed to my room and, counting the minutes, grabbed a book, leafed through it and found an illustration of a tracheotomy. Everything about it was clear and simple: the throat was laid open and the knife plunged into the windpipe. I started reading the text, but could take none of it in – the words seemed to jump before my eyes. I had never seen a tracheotomy performed. 'Ah well, it's a bit late now,' I said to myself, and looked miserably at the green lamp and the clear illustration. Feeling that I had suddenly been burdened with a most fearful and difficult task, I went back to the hospital, oblivious of the snowstorm.

In the surgery a dim figure in full skirts clung to me and a voice whined:

'Oh, sir, how can you cut a little girl's throat? How can you? She's agreed to it because she's stupid. But you haven't got my permission – no you haven't. I agree to giving her medicine, but I shan't allow her throat to be cut.'

'Get this woman out!' I shouted, and added vehemently: 'You're the stupid one! Yes, you are. And she's the clever one. Anyway, nobody asked you! Get her out of here!'

A midwife took a firm hold of the old woman and pushed her out of the room.

'Ready!' the *feldsher* said suddenly.

We went into the small operating theatre; the shiny instruments, blinding lamplight and oilcloth seemed to belong to another world . . . for the last time I went out to the mother, and the little girl could scarcely be torn from her arms. She just said in a hoarse voice: 'My husband's away in town. When he comes back and finds out what I've done, he'll kill me!'

'Yes, he'll kill her,' the old woman echoed, looking at me in horror.

'Don't let them into the operating theatre!' I ordered.

So we were left in the operating theatre, my assistants, myself, and Lidka, the little girl. She sat naked and pathetic on the table and wept soundlessly. They laid her on the table, strapped her down, washed her throat and painted it with iodine. I picked up the scalpel, still wondering what on earth I was doing. It

47

was very quiet. With the scalpel I made a vertical incision down the swollen white throat. Not one drop of blood emerged. Again I drew the knife along the white strip which protruded between the slit skin. Again not a trace of blood. Slowly, trying to remember the illustrations in my textbooks, I started to part the delicate tissues with the blunt probe. At once dark blood gushed out from the lower end of the wound, flooding it instantly and pouring down her neck. The *feldsher* started to staunch it with swabs but could not stop the flow. Calling to mind everything I had seen at university, I set about clamping the edges of the wound with forceps, but this did no good either.

I went cold and my forehead broke out in a sweat. I bitterly regretted having studied medicine and having landed myself in this wilderness. In angry desperation I jabbed the forceps haphazardly into the region of the wound, snapped them shut and the flow of blood stopped immediately. We swabbed the wound with pieces of gauze; now it faced me clean and absolutely incomprehensible. There was no windpipe anywhere to be seen. This wound of mind was quite unlike any illustration. I spent the next two or three minutes aimlessly poking about the wound, first with the scalpel and then with the probe, searching for the windpipe. After two minutes of this, I despaired of finding it. 'This is the end,' I thought. 'Why did I ever do this? I needn't have offered to do the operation, and Lidka could have died quietly in the ward. As it is she will die with her throat slit open and I can never prove that she would have died anyway, that I couldn't have made it any worse . . .' The midwife wiped my brow in silence. 'I ought to put down my scalpel and say: I don't know what to do next.' As I thought this I pictured the mother's eyes. I picked up the knife again and made a deep, undirected slash into Lidka's neck. The tissues parted and to my surprise the windpipe appeared before me.

'Hooks!' I croaked hoarsely.

The *feldsher* handed them to me. I pierced each side with a hook and handed one of them to him. Now I could see one thing only: the greyish ringlets of the windpipe. I thrust the sharp knife into it – and froze in horror. The windpipe was coming out of the incision and the *feldsher* appeared to have taken leave of his wits: he was tearing it out. Behind me the midwives gasped. I looked up and saw what was the matter: the *feldsher* had fainted from the oppressive heat and, still holding the hook, was tearing at the windpipe. 'It's fate,' I thought, 'everything's against me. We've certainly murdered Lidka now.' And I added grimly to myself: 'As soon as I get back to my room, I'll shoot myself.' Then the older midwife, who was evidently very experienced, pounced on the *feldsher* and tore the hook out of his hand, saying through her clenched teeth:

'Go on, doctor . . .'

The *feldsher* collapsed to the floor with a crash but we did not turn to look at him. I plunged the scalpel into the trachea and then inserted a silver tube. It slid in easily but Lidka remained motionless. The air did not flow into her windpipe as it should have done. I sighed deeply and stopped: I had done all I could. I felt like begging someone's forgiveness for having been so thoughtless as to study medicine. Silence reigned. I could see Lidka turning blue. I was just about to give up and weep, when the child suddenly gave a violent convulsion, expelled a fountain of disgusting clotted matter through the tube, and the air whistled into her windpipe. As she started to breathe, the little girl began to howl. That instant the *feldsher* got to his feet, pale and sweaty, looked at her throat in stupefied horror and helped me to sew it up.

Dazed, my vision blurred by a film of sweat, I saw the happy faces of the midwives and one of them said to me:

'You did the operation brilliantly, doctor.'

I thought she was making fun of me and glowered at her. Then the doors were opened and a gust of fresh air blew in. Lidka was carried out wrapped in a sheet and at once the mother appeared in the doorway. Her eyes had the look of a wild beast. She asked me:

'Well?'

When I heard the sound of her voice, I felt a cold sweat run down my back as I realised what it would have been like if Lidka had died on the table. But I answered her in a very calm voice:

'Don't worry, she's alive. And she'll stay alive, I hope. Only she won't be able to talk until we take the pipe out, so don't let that upset you.'

Just then the grandmother seemed to materialise from nowhere and crossed herself, bowing to the doorhandle, to me, and to the ceiling. This time I did not lose my temper with her, I turned away and ordered Lidka to be given a camphor injection and for the staff to take turns at watching her. Then I went across the yard to my quarters. I remember the green lamp burning in my study, Döderlein lying there and books scattered everywhere. I walked over to the couch fully dressed, lay down and was immediately lost to the world in a dreamless sleep.

A month passed, then another. I grew more experienced and some of the things I saw were rather more frightening than Lidka's throat, which passed out of my mind. Snow lay all around, and the size of my practice grew daily. Early in the new year, a woman came to my surgery holding by the hand a little girl wrapped in so many layers that she looked as round as a little barrel. The woman's eyes were shining. I took a good look and recognised them.

'Ah, Lidka! How are things?'

'Everything's fine.'

The mother unwound the scarves from Lidka's neck. Though she was shy and resisted I managed to raise her chin and took a look. Her pink neck was marked with a brown vertical scar crossed by two fine stitch marks.

'All's well,' I said. 'You needn't come any more.'

'Thank you, doctor, thank you,' the mother said, and turned to Lidka: 'Say thank you to the gentleman!'

But Lidka had no wish to speak to me.

I never saw her again. Gradually I forgot about her. Meanwhile my practice still grew. The day came when I had a hundred and ten patients. We began at nine in the morning and finished at eight in the evening. Reeling with fatigue, I was taking off my overall when the senior midwife said to me:

'It's the tracheotomy that has brought you all these patients. Do you know what they're saying in the villages? The story goes that when Lidka was ill a steel throat was put into her instead of her own and then sewn up. People go to her village especially to look at her. There's fame for you, doctor. Congratulations.'

'So they think she's living with a steel one now, do they?' I enquired.

'That's right. But you were wonderful, doctor. You did it so coolly, it was marvellous to watch.'

'Hm, well, I never allow myself to worry, you know,' I said, not knowing why. I was too tired even to feel ashamed, so I just looked away. I said goodnight and went home. Snow was falling in large flakes, covering everything, the lantern was lit and my house looked silent, solitary and imposing. As I walked I had only one desire – sleep.

51

*- 1st person narration => more involved in action,*
*subjective in what narr. think.*
*-draws into plot*

# Focus on context

*Why did he drive in case of discrimination*

Discuss ō Father's decision to Drive to mississippi
effects, results, conseq. of trip.
Status, identity

# The Gold Cadillac

## by Mildred D. Taylor

*mother => Strong headed/willed, has own stand, president => dan-to-earth*

My sister and I were playing out on the front lawn when the gold Cadillac rolled up and my father stepped from behind the wheel. We ran to him, our eyes filled with wonder. 'Daddy, whose Cadillac?' I asked.

And Wilma demanded, 'Where's our Mercury?'

My father grinned. 'Go get your mother and I'll tell you all about it.'

'Is it ours?' I cried. 'Daddy, is it ours?'

'Get your mother!' he laughed. 'And tell her to hurry!'

Wilma and I ran off to obey as Mr Pondexter next door came from his house to see what this new Cadillac was all about. We threw open the front door, ran through the downstairs front parlour and straight through the house to the kitchen where my mother was cooking and one of my aunts was helping her. 'Come on, Mother-Dear!' we cried together. 'Daddy say come on out and see this new car!'

'What?' said my mother, her face showing her surprise. 'What're you talking about?'

'A Cadillac!' I cried.

'He said hurry up!' relayed Wilma.

And then we took off again, up the back stairs to the second floor of the duplex. Running down the hall, we banged on all the apartment doors. My uncles and their wives stepped to the doors. It was good it was a Saturday morning. Everybody was home.

'We got us a Cadillac! We got us a Cadillac!' Wilma and I proclaimed in unison. We had decided that the Cadillac had to be ours if our father was driving it and holding on to the keys. 'Come on see!' Then we raced on, through the upstairs sunroom, down the front steps, through the downstairs sunroom, and out to the Cadillac. Mr Pondexter was still there. Mr LeRoy and Mr Courtland from down the street were there too and all were admiring the Cadillac as my father stood proudly by, pointing out the various features.

'Brand-new 1950 Coup deVille!' I heard one of the men saying.

'Just off the showroom floor!' my father said. 'I just couldn't resist it.'

My sister and I eased up to the car and peeked in. It was all gold inside. Gold leather seats. Gold carpeting. Gold dashboard. It was like no car we had owned before. It looked like a car for rich folks.

'Daddy, are we rich?' I asked. My father laughed.

'Daddy, it's ours, isn't it?' asked Wilma, who was older and more practical than I. She didn't intend to give her heart too quickly to something that wasn't hers.

'You like it?'

'Oh, Daddy, yes!'

He looked at me. 'What 'bout you, 'lois?'

'Yes, sir!'

My father laughed again. 'Then I expect I can't much disappoint my girls, can I? It's ours all right!'

Wilma and I hugged our father with our joy. My uncles came from the house and my aunts, carrying their babies, came out too. Everybody surrounded the car and owwed and ahhed. Nobody could believe it.

Then my mother came out.

Everybody stood back grinning as she approached the car. There was no smile on her face. We all waited for her to speak. She stared at the car, then looked at my father, standing there as proud as he could be. Finally she said, 'You didn't buy this car, did you, Wilbert?'

'Gotta admit I did. Couldn't resist it.'

'But . . . but what about our Mercury? It was perfectly good!'

'Don't you like the Cadillac, Dee?'

'That Mercury wasn't even a year old!'

My father nodded. 'And I'm sure whoever buys it is going to get themselves a good car. But we've got ourselves a better one. Now stop frowning, honey, and let's take ourselves a ride in our brand-new Cadillac!'

My mother shook her head. 'I've got food on the stove,' she said and turning away walked back to the house.

There was an awkward silence and then my father said, 'You know Dee never did much like surprises. Guess this here Cadillac was a bit too much for her. I best go smooth things out with her.' -sensitive

Everybody watched as he went after my mother. But when he came back, he was alone.

'Well, what she say?' asked one of my uncles.

My father shrugged and smiled. 'Told me I bought this Cadillac alone, I could just ride in it alone.'

Another uncle laughed. 'Uh-oh! Guess she told you!'

'Oh, she'll come around,' said one of my aunts. 'Any woman would be proud to ride in this car.'

'That's what I'm banking on,' said my father as he went around to the street side of the car and opened the door. 'All right! Who's for a ride?'

'We are!' Wilma and I cried.

All three of my uncles and one of my aunts, still holding her baby, and Mr Pondexter climbed in with us and we took off for the first ride in the gold Cadillac. It was a glorious ride and we drove all through the city of Toledo. We rode past the church and past the school. We rode through Ottawa Hills where the rich folks lived and on into Walbridge Park and past the zoo, then along the Maumee River. But none of us had had enough of the car so my father put the car on the road and we drove all the way to Detroit. We had plenty of family there and everybody was just as pleased as could be about the Cadillac. My father told our Detroit relatives that he was in the doghouse with my mother about buying the Cadillac. My uncles told them she wouldn't ride in the car. All the Detroit family thought that was funny and everybody, including my father, laughed about it and said my mother would come around.

It was early evening by the time we got back home, and I could see from my mother's face she had not come around. She was angry now not only about the car, but that we had been gone so long. I didn't understand that, since my father had called her as soon as we reached Detroit to let her know where we were. I had heard him myself. I didn't understand either why she did not like that fine Cadillac and thought she was being terribly disagreeable with my father. That night as she tucked Wilma and me in bed I told her that too.

'Is this your business?' she asked.

'Well, I just think you ought to be nice to Daddy. I think you ought to ride in that car with him! It'd sure make him happy.'

'I think you ought to go to sleep,' she said and turned out the light.

Later I heard her arguing with my father. 'We're supposed to be saving for a house!' she said.

'We've already got a house!' said my father.

'But you said you wanted a house in a better neighbourhood. I thought that's what we both said!'

'I haven't changed my mind.'

'Well, you have a mighty funny way of saving for it, then. Your brothers are saving for houses of their own and you don't see them out buying new cars every year!'

'We'll still get the house, Dee. That's a promise!'

'Not with new Cadillacs we won't!' said my mother and then she said a very loud good night and all was quiet.

The next day was Sunday and everybody figured that my mother would be sure to give in and ride in the Cadillac. After all, the family always went to church together on Sunday. But she didn't give in. What was worse she wouldn't let Wilma and me ride in the Cadillac either. She took us each by the hand, walked past the Cadillac where my father stood waiting and headed on towards the church, three blocks away. I was really mad at her now. I had been looking forward to driving up to the church in that gold Cadillac and having everybody see.

On most Sunday afternoons during the summertime, my mother, my father, Wilma, and I would go for a ride. Sometimes we just rode around the city and visited friends and family. Sometimes we made short trips over to Chicago or Peoria or Detroit to see relatives there or to Cleveland where we had relatives too, but we could also see the Cleveland Indians play. Sometimes we joined our aunts and uncles and drove in a caravan out to the park or to the beach. At the park or the beach Wilma and I would run and play. My mother and my aunts would spread a picnic and my father and my uncles would shine their cars.

But on this Sunday afternoon my mother refused to ride anywhere. She told Wilma and me that we could go. So we left her alone in the big, empty house, and the family cars, led by the gold Cadillac, headed for the park. For a while I played and had a good time, but then I stopped playing and went to sit with my father. Despite his laughter he seemed sad to me. I think he was missing my mother as much as I was.

That evening my father took my mother to dinner down at the corner café. They walked. Wilma and I stayed at the house chasing fireflies in the back yard. My aunts and uncles sat in the yard and on the porch, talking and laughing about the day and watching us. It was a soft summer's evening, the kind that came every day and was expected. The smell of charcoal and of barbecue drifting from up the block, the sound of laughter and music and talk drifting from yard to yard were all a part of it. Soon one of my uncles joined Wilma and me in our chase of fireflies and when my mother and father came home we were at it still. My mother and father watched us for a while, while everybody else watched them to see if my father would take out the Cadillac and if my mother would slide in beside him to take a ride. But it soon became evident that the dinner had not changed my mother's mind. She still refused to ride in the Cadillac. I just couldn't understand her objection to it.

Though my mother didn't like the Cadillac, everybody else in the neighbourhood certainly did. That meant quite a few folks too, since we lived on a very busy block. On one corner was a grocery store, a cleaner's, and a gas station. Across the street was a beauty shop and a fish market, and down the street was a bar, another grocery store, the Dixie Theatre, the café, and a drugstore. There were always people strolling to or from one of these places and because our house was right in the middle of the block just about everybody had to pass our house and the gold Cadillac. Sometimes people took in the Cadillac as they walked, their heads turning for a longer look as they passed. Then there were people who just outright stopped and took a good look before continuing on their way. I was proud to say that car belonged to my family. I felt mighty important as people called to me as I ran down the street. ''Ey, 'lois! How's that Cadillac, girl? Riding fine?' I told my mother how much everybody liked that car. She was not impressed and made no comment.

Since just about everybody on the block knew everybody else, most folks knew that my mother wouldn't ride in the Cadillac. Because of that, my father took a lot of good-natured kidding from the men. My mother got kidded too as the women said if she didn't ride in that car, maybe some other woman would. And everybody laughed about it and began to bet on who would give in first, my mother or my father. But then my father said he was going to drive the car south into Mississippi to visit my grandparents and everybody stopped laughing.

My uncles stopped.

So did my aunts.

Everybody.

'Look here, Wilbert,' said one of my uncles, 'it's too dangerous. It's like putting a loaded gun to your head.'

'I paid good money for that car,' said my father. 'That gives me a right to drive it where I please. Even down to Mississippi.'

My uncles argued with him and tried to talk him out of driving the car south. So did my aunts and so did the neighbours, Mr LeRoy, Mr Courtland and Mr Pondexter. They said it was a dangerous thing, a mighty dangerous thing, for a black man to drive an expensive car into the rural South.

'Not much those folks hate more'n to see a northern Negro coming down there in a fine car,' said Mr Pondexter. 'They see those Ohio licence plates, they'll figure you coming down uppity, trying to lord your fine car over them!'

I listened, but I didn't understand. I didn't understand why they didn't want my father to drive that car south. It was his.

'Listen to Pondexter, Wilbert!' cried another uncle. 'We might've fought a war to free people overseas, but we're not free here! Man, those white folks down south'll lynch you soon's look at you. You know that!'

Wilma and I looked at each other. Neither one of us knew what *lynch* meant, but the word sent a shiver through us. We held each other's hand.

My father was silent, then he said: 'All my life I've had to be heedful of what white folks thought. Well, I'm tired of that. I worked hard for everything I got. Got it honest, too. Now I got that Cadillac because I liked it and because it meant something to me that somebody like me from Mississippi could go and buy it. It's my car, I paid for it, and I'm driving it south.'

My mother, who had said nothing through all this, now stood. 'Then the girls and I'll be going too,' she said.

'No!' said my father.

My mother only looked at him and went off to the kitchen.

My father shook his head. It seemed he didn't want us to go. My uncles looked at each other, then at my father. 'You set on doing this, we'll all go,' they said.

'That way we can watch out for each other.' My father took a moment and nodded. Then my aunts got up and went off to their kitchens too.

All the next day my aunts and my mother cooked and the house was filled with delicious smells. They fried chicken and baked hams and cakes and sweet potato pies and mixed potato salad. They filled jugs with water and punch and coffee. Then they packed everything in huge picnic baskets along with bread and boiled eggs, oranges and apples, plates and napkins, spoons and forks and cups. They placed all that food on the back seats of the cars. It was like a grand, grand picnic we were going on, and Wilma and I were mighty excited. We could hardly wait to start.

My father, my mother, Wilma and I got into the Cadillac. My uncles, my aunts, my cousins got into the Ford, the Buick, and the Chevrolet, and we rolled off in our caravan headed south. Though my mother was finally riding in the Cadillac, she had no praise for it. In fact, she said nothing about it at all. She still seemed upset and since she still seemed to feel the same about the car, I wondered why she had insisted upon making this trip with my father.

We left the city of Toledo behind, drove through Bowling Green and down through the Ohio countryside of farms and small towns, through Dayton and Cincinnati, and across the Ohio River into Kentucky. On the other side of the river my father stopped the car and looked back at Wilma and me and said, 'Now from here on, whenever we stop and there're white people around, I don't want either one of you to say a word. *Not one word!* Your mother and I'll do all the talking. That understood?'

'Yes, sir,' Wilma and I both said, though we didn't truly understand why.

My father nodded, looked at my mother and started the car again. We rolled on, down Highway 25 and through the bluegrass hills of Kentucky. Soon we began to see signs. Signs that read: WHITE ONLY, COLOURED NOT ALLOWED. Hours later, we left the Bluegrass State and crossed into Tennessee. Now we saw even more of the signs saying: WHITE ONLY, COLOURED NOT ALLOWED. We saw signs above water fountains and in restaurant windows. We saw them in ice-cream parlours and at hamburger stands. We saw them in front of hotels and motels, and on the restroom doors of filling stations. I didn't like the signs. I felt as if I were in a foreign land.

I couldn't understand why the signs were there and I asked my father what the signs meant. He said they meant we couldn't drink from the water fountains. He said they meant we couldn't stop to sleep in the motels. He said they meant we couldn't stop to eat in the restaurants. I looked at the grand picnic basket I had been enjoying so much. Now I understood why my mother had packed it. Suddenly the picnic did not seem so grand.

Finally we reached Memphis. We got there at a bad time. Traffic was heavy and we got separated from the rest of the family. We tried to find them but it was no use. We had to go on alone. We reached the Mississippi state line and soon after we heard a police siren. A police car came up behind us. My father slowed the Cadillac, then stopped. Two white policemen got out of their car. They eyeballed the Cadillac and told my father to get out.

'Whose car is this, boy?' they asked.

I saw anger in my father's eyes. 'It's mine,' he said.

'You're a liar,' said one of the policemen. 'You stole this car.'

'Turn around, put your hands on top of that car and spread-eagle,' said the other policeman.

My father did as he was told. They searched him and I didn't understand why. I didn't understand either why they had called my father a liar and didn't believe that the Cadillac was his. I wanted to ask but I remembered my father's warning not to say a word and I obeyed that warning.

The policemen told my father to get in the back of the police car. My father did. One policeman got back into the police car. The other policeman slid behind the wheel of our Cadillac. The police car started off. The Cadillac followed. Wilma and I looked at each other and at our mother. We didn't know what to think. We were scared.

The Cadillac followed the police car into a small town and stopped in front of the police station. The policeman stepped out of our Cadillac and took the keys. The other policeman took my father into the police station.

'Mother-Dear!' Wilma and I cried. 'What're they going to do to our daddy? They going to hurt him?'

'He'll be all right,' said my mother. 'He'll be all right.' But she didn't sound so sure of that. She seemed worried.

We waited. More than three hours we waited. Finally my father came out of the police station. We had lots of questions to ask him. He said the police had given him a ticket for speeding and locked him up. But then the judge had come. My father had paid the ticket and they had let him go.

He started the Cadillac and drove slowly out of the town, below the speed limit. The police car followed us. People standing on steps and sitting on porches and in front of stores stared at us as we passed. Finally we were out of the town. The police car still followed. Dusk was falling. The night grew black and finally the police car turned around and left us.

We drove and drove. But my father was tired now and my grandparents' farm was still far away. My father said he had to get some sleep and since my mother didn't drive, he pulled into a grove of trees at the side of the road and stopped.

'I'll keep watch,' said my mother.

'Wake me if you see anybody,' said my father.

'Just rest,' said my mother.

So my father slept. But that bothered me. I needed him awake. I was afraid of the dark and of the woods and of whatever lurked there. My father was the one who kept us safe, he and my uncles. But already the police had taken my father away from us once today and my uncles were lost.

'Go to sleep, baby,' said my mother. 'Go to sleep.'

But I was afraid to sleep until my father woke. I had to help my mother keep watch. I figured I had to help protect us too, in case the police came back and tried to take my father away again. There was a long, sharp knife in the picnic basket and I took hold of it, clutching it tightly in my hand. Ready to strike, I sat there in the back of the car, eyes wide, searching the blackness outside the Cadillac. Wilma, for a while, searched the night too, then she fell asleep. I didn't want to sleep, but soon I found I couldn't help myself as an unwelcome drowsiness came over me. I had an uneasy sleep and when I woke it was dawn and my father was gently shaking me. I woke with a start and my hand went up, but the knife wasn't there. My mother had it.

My father took my hand. 'Why were you holding the knife, 'lois?' he asked.

I looked at him and at my mother. 'I – I was scared,' I said.

My father was thoughtful. 'No need to be scared now, sugar,' he said. 'Daddy's here and so is Mother-Dear.' Then after a glance at my mother, he got out of the car, walked to the road, looked down it one way, then the other. When he came back and started the motor, he turned the Cadillac north, not south.

'What're you doing?' asked my mother.

'Heading back to Memphis,' said my father. 'Cousin Halton's there. We'll leave the Cadillac and get his car. Driving this car any farther south with you and the girls in the car, it's just not worth the risk.'

And so that's what we did. Instead of driving through Mississippi in golden splendour, we travelled its streets and roads and highways in Cousin Halton's solid, yet not so splendid, four-year-old Chevy. When we reached my grandparents' farm, my uncles and aunts were already there. Everybody was glad to see us. They had been worried. They asked about the Cadillac. My father told them what had happened, and they nodded and said he had done the best thing.

We stayed one week in Mississippi. During that week I often saw my father, looking deep in thought, walk off alone across the family land. I saw my mother watching him. One day I ran after my father, took his hand, and walked the land with him. I asked him all the questions that were on my mind. I asked him why the policemen had treated him the way they had and why people didn't want us to eat in the restaurants or drink from the water fountains or sleep in the hotels. I told him I just didn't understand all that.

My father looked at me and said that it all was a difficult thing to understand and he didn't really understand it himself. He said it all had to do with the fact that black people had once been forced to be slaves. He said it had to do with our skins being coloured. He said it had to do with stupidity and ignorance. He said it had to do with the law, the law that said we could be treated like this here in the South. And for that matter, he added, any other place in these United States where folks thought the same as so many folks did here in the South. But he also said, 'I'm hoping one day though we can drive that long road down here and there won't be any signs. I'm hoping one day the police won't stop us just because of the colour of our skins and we're riding in a gold Cadillac with northern plates.'

When the week ended, we said good-bye to my grandparents and all the Mississippi family and headed in a caravan back towards Memphis. In Memphis we returned Cousin Halton's car and got our Cadillac. Once we were home my father put the Cadillac in the garage and didn't drive it. I didn't hear my mother say any more about the Cadillac. I didn't hear my father speak of it either.

Some days passed and then on a bright Saturday afternoon while Wilma and I were playing in the back yard, I saw my father go into the garage. He opened the garage doors wide so the sunshine streamed in, and began to shine the Cadillac. I saw my mother at the kitchen window staring out across the yard at my father. For a long time, she stood there watching my father shine his car. Then she came out and crossed the yard to the garage and I heard her say, 'Wilbert, you keep the car.'

He looked at her as if he had not heard.

'You keep it,' she repeated and turned and walked back to the house.

My father watched her until the back door had shut

behind her. Then he went on shining the car and soon began to sing. About an hour later he got into the car and drove away. That evening when he came back he was walking. The Cadillac was nowhere in sight.

'Daddy, where's our new Cadillac?' I demanded to know. So did Wilma.

He smiled and put his hand on my head. 'Sold it,' he said as my mother came into the room.

'But how come?' I asked. 'We poor now?'

'No, sugar. We've got more money towards our new house now and we're all together. I figure that makes us about the richest folks in the world.' He smiled at my mother and she smiled too and came into his arms.

After that we drove around in an old 1930s Model A Ford my father had. He said he'd factory-ordered us another Mercury, this time with my mother's approval. Despite that, most folks on the block figured we had fallen on hard times after such a splashy showing of good times and some folks even laughed at us as the Ford rattled around the city. I must admit that at first I was pretty much embarrassed to be riding around in that old Ford after the splendour of the Cadillac. But my father said to hold my head high. We and the family knew the truth. As fine as the Cadillac had been, he said, it had pulled us apart for a while. Now, as ragged and noisy as that old Ford was, we all rode in it together and we were a family again. So I held my head high.

Still though, I often thought of that Cadillac. We had had the Cadillac only a little more than a month, but I wouldn't soon forget its splendour or how I'd felt riding around inside it. I wouldn't soon forget either the ride we had taken south in it. I wouldn't soon forget the signs, the policemen, or my fear. I would remember that ride and the gold Cadillac all my life.

# Poinsettias

**by Beverley Naidoo**

Marika thrust the glass jar up to Veronica's face.

'See this one Nicky!' she declared. 'Caught it last week!' Veronica stared at the coiled brown shape slithering inside the greenish liquid. She felt sick.

'You should have seen how blinking quick I was man! This sort are poisonous!'

Marika's eyes pinned her down, watching for a reaction. She didn't know which were worse, Marika's or those of the dead creature in the jar.

'Where did you find it?'

Her voice did not betray her and Marika began her dramatic tale about tracking the snake in the bougainvillaea next to the hen-run.

It was a valuable addition to her collection. Rows of bottles, all with the same green liquid, lined the shelf above her bed. Spiders and insects of various shapes and sizes floated safely, serenely, inside. Marika carefully replaced the snake next to another prize item – a one-legged chameleon, its colours dulled and fixed. Veronica remembered it alive. It had been the farm children's pet briefly until they had tired of capturing flies for it. She had even helped one whole Saturday, prowling around the cow-shed, sneaking up and snapping the over-fed blue-buzzers in cigarette tins. The next morning Marika and her brothers had decided to let the creature go free and get its own dinner. But when they had come to release the catch of

67

the splintering old wood-and-wire hutch, the chameleon lay stiff and still. The three boys had wanted to make a special grave down in the donga – but in the end Marika had persuaded them to let her preserve it.

The farm, a small-holding owned by Marika's parents, lay against a mountain in the middle of the Magaliesberg. As well as growing fruit and vegetables and keeping a few animals, the van Reenens let out a small cottage on the farm, mostly to city visitors. It was near enough to Johannesburg for Mr and Mrs Martin with their only child Veronica to get away from the ever-increasing hustle for short breaks. They were regulars, coming two or three times a year. In fact Mr Martin had been visiting since he was a child, when Marika's mother herself had been a small girl on the same farm. Veronica's own memories of the place stretched back for as long as she could remember. For years she and Marika had played 'house' in the donga behind the farmhouse. They had used larger stones for the walls, shifting around smaller stones as the furniture. In the past Veronica used to bring all her dolls, despite her mother's protests. Sensing Marika's envy, she had enjoyed saying which dolls could be played with. But since Marika's tenth birthday things were different.

Veronica had been taken by surprise. She had been sitting with the farm children on the wall of the stoep, dangling her legs and kicking the brickwork with her heels like the others. Marika had been telling her about the disco which had been her birthday treat when Veronica had suggested that they go to the donga.

'Hey the girls are going to play dollies!' Marika's twin brother Piet had sneered. Slipping off the wall, six-year-old Dirk had rolled on the ground, kicking his legs in the air and cooing.

'Gaga gaga! Mommy! Mommy! Change my nappy!'

Veronica had glared at him and he had pulled a face at her. She had fought to hold back her tears. Only Anton, the oldest, had not joined in, but called the others to leave the girls alone to their sissy games. Marika had reacted furiously.

'I'm not a sissy!' she had screamed after them. Leaving Veronica alone on the stoep, she had gone inside the house, slamming the door behind her.

When Veronica returned to the farm a few months later, Marika had begun her bottle collection. Veronica had also left her dolls at home, except for the eyelid-clicking, brown-eyed Margaret. But this time the porcelain head with brown painted curls remained tucked under the bedclothes and was spoken to only at night. She became Veronica's personal counsellor on the farm – a pale replica of Veronica's personal counsellor in town.

Back home in Johannesburg it was Rebecca, their maid, to whom Veronica confided. She was a far better listener than Margaret because she made sympathetic noises. With Veronica's mother often helping out at her father's office, or busy with Mothers' Union meetings, they spent a lot of time together. Whether she was cooking, washing, ironing or dusting, Rebecca was always prepared to chat. But she never came to the farm with them. Instead she went to visit her own children, living with their grandmother, a five-hour bus ride away.

-Sharing secrets with Rebecca was fun, especially when Rebecca had let her visit her dim, tiny room in the servants' quarters at the top of their block of flats. It had started with her desperate desire to see the bedspread which Rebecca had been patiently embroidering for months on 'babysitting' nights when

Veronica's parents went out. Although Veronica didn't
think she needed to be 'babysat', she liked Rebecca's
company. Together they would sit and talk at the table
in the Martin's kitchen until it was her bed-time. She
had watched the bedspread growing and, when it was
finally completed, had begged and nagged to see how
it looked on the bed. But before she could be taken,
Rebecca had made her promise, 'Remember, you are
not to tell your ma or pa!'

Because it had been a secret, everything had stayed
fixed in her mind like a picture. The splendid
bedcover draped over an old iron bed raised up high
on bricks. A curtain across one corner of the room.
Rebecca's cupboard. An orange crate table next to the
bed, on which stood a photo of Rebecca's four
children. Veronica had studied their smiling black
faces to see if they looked like their mother, trying to
match the faces to the names she asked Rebecca to
repeat. The only one whose name she always
remembered was Selo, the oldest, because he was
exactly her age and his name was shorter than the
others.

'Is this Selo?' she had asked, picking out the tallest
of the children, who had a cheerful, cheeky grin.

'Oh yes, that's Selo! Always getting into trouble!'
Rebecca had laughed, adding, 'But he's a good boy.'

Yet here on the farm there was no Rebecca. So it was to
Margaret that Veronica confided about the snake's
awful eyes. Of course if it was Rebecca, she would make
some sounds to show how disgusted she was. Then they
would laugh together at how stupid it was to keep all
those dead creatures in jars.

But there was something even more important she
needed to talk to Rebecca about. It was something

Marika had said after she had put the snake back on the shelf. She had hinted strongly that her brothers had made up a test which Veronica would have to pass before she could go on playing with them. Marika herself had carried out a dare set by the boys. She would not say what it had been, it was so terrible. She was equally mysterious about Veronica's dare.

'I'm not allowed to tell . . . but you know our neighbour Jan Venter . . .?'

Marika had stopped and ominously refused to say anything more.

Big and burly – known for his flaming red beard, moustache and temper – children, and even adults, usually kept clear of Meneer Venter when possible. Veronica had seen him only once, when he had called to see Mr van Reenen to insist Marika's father mend the fence between them. He ran one of the biggest orange estates in the area and everyone knew that he threatened to shoot any trespasser on his land like he shot baboons. That was not to be taken lightly. Jan Venter was known to be 'fond of the bottle' and there had been talk about the disappearance of Mrs Venter a few years ago. Some people said she had just had enough of his temper and gone back to her own people in another part of the country. The rumour amongst the local children was that he had murdered his wife and buried her in front of his house – under a poinsettia bush which now had brighter than usual red flowers.

The next morning, instead of darting off early to look for Marika, Veronica hung back and waited for her parents before going to the farmhouse for breakfast. Marika and her family ate in the kitchen but the Martins were served their meals in the dining-room, beneath a pair of massive kudu horns and heavily framed photographs of Marika's grandparents. Mrs van Reenen followed behind the servant who carried the plates of steaming porridge.

'Still no sign of rain, but it'll be a nice day again for you all!'

She smiled and stopped to pass on some of the local news, including talk of a leopard seen again on the mountain behind the farm.

Today Veronica took her time. When she came to her last piece of toast, she chewed it slowly. She was trying to think of a good reason to stay with her parents who were pouring second cups of coffee, when her mother said, 'You can be excused, Veronica dear. You can go off and play. You won't go near the mountain, will you?' *—danger if she goes to Venter's plantation more dangerous.*

She nodded, pursing her lips together and got up. Her father ruffled her hair as she passed.

'Have a good day Ronnie!' *name calling. Supposed to be intimacy*

He only called her that when he was relaxed. She just hoped Marika's brothers didn't ever hear it. Their jokes about 'Nicky' were bad enough. *name calling → childishness*

Hoping the van Reenen children might still be at breakfast in the kitchen, Veronica headed for the opposite door, to the stoep. But they were already there on the wall, legs swinging, waiting. Anton, the oldest, was direct.

'We've made a new rule. Girls have to do a dare before they join our gang.'

Veronica stood rooted to the concrete floor. All the children except Anton were grinning. Dead-pan, he went on to explain that she had to climb through the barbed-wire fence into the neighbouring Venter estate and make her way across to the front of Jan Venter's farmhouse.

'You've got to get one of his poinsettia flowers. We

don't have any this side, so you can't cheat!'

They would accompany her as far as the fence and wait for her to return.

There was no way out. If she wasn't part of the gang, there would be no one to play with. As they marched across the donga Veronica glanced at the spot where they used to play 'house' in the shade of the thorn trees. The stones were still there. It was like another world. Inside she felt cold and shivery even though her feet and arms were moving swiftly in step with the others and the sun's heat was already enveloping them. As they trudged in silence along the edge of the mealie field, nearing the wire fence, Dirk suddenly broke out into a jingle.

'Nicky, Nicky, looks so sicky!' insensivity of children — cride remarks

He was told sharply to shut up by the others.

'A dare is not a game! It's a serious thing you idiot,' Marika snapped.

At the fence Anton and Piet parted the barbed wire for Veronica to slip through. Anton pointed.

'The farmhouse is that way. At the end of the orange trees follow the road.'

Veronica cast a quick glimpse back at the group. They all had solemn faces except for Dirk who couldn't hide his little grin. She was already far down the line of orange trees when she heard Marika's voice ringing faintly behind her.

'Good luck, hey Nicky!'

Sounds of laughter seemed to follow.

For as far as she could see ahead there were only straight rows of trees, the deep green leaves and bright orange fruit silently glinting in the sunlight. They were not good cover. With her shadow darting from one tree's patch of shade to the next, her mind began searching wildly for what to say if she was caught.

Could she pretend she was lost . . . or that she had a dog which had got lost? Or that she had come to warn Meneer Venter about the leopard on the mountain? Veronica could not imagine the big burly man with the flaming beard believing any of her stories. She almost wished the dare had been for her to go up the mountain instead.

Her mouth was dry, her body wet and sticky, her legs sprinting heavily. Sucking in small quick breaths, she jerked to a halt. The moments of rest brought a terrible panic. What on earth was she doing here, alone in the middle of Jan Venter's oranges? This dare was too dangerous. She should run back and tell the others it was unfair. She bet they wouldn't do it! Then she remembered Marika saying her own dare was too terrible to talk about. Perhaps she had just said that to frighten her . . . But if she went back now, that would be the end of their friendship. Whatever could she do by herself on the farm? It wasn't worth thinking about. Lips pressed together, her eyes intently scoured the bushes ahead.

At last she could see she was coming to a dirt road. Peering from behind a tree, she studied how to make her way up it. On either side was a line of tall grey bluegums leading to a cluster of white-washed buildings. The furthest one seemed to be the main house. There was no poinsettia in sight, so the front had to be around one of the other sides. Behind the bluegums on the far side of the road, set a little back, were some huts – servants' quarters. Usually she hardly took any notice of these kind of buildings. They were just there, part of what you found on a farm. But now she was forced to scan the area around the huts very closely. Although there were some open doorways, they were too dark to see inside. No one seemed to be around, either on the road or in the workers' compound, but it would be safer to stay on the side where she was for as long as possible. A few large avocado trees would provide thick cover for a short stretch – and then she would have to trust to the bluegums and to fortune.

At last, in line with the main house, she crossed the road. Her shoes smacking against the sand pounded as loudly as her heart. Facing her was a door, leading to a backyard. She ducked down to creep past a window. A few paces more and she had reached the side of the raised stoep. On tip-toe she stretched to look. Still no one! Through the wooden railings she glimpsed a spray of pointed red flowers. The poinsettia was just around the corner! Making a final dash to the bush, she ripped off a flower at the stem. Milky white stuff spurted out on to her fingers. Not bothering to wipe off the stickiness, she turned to run. But a door banging and fearsome shouting forced her to cower back next to the poinsettia bush and freeze.

'Jou bliksem! Ek sal jou moer!'

It could only be Jan Venter. Veronica's Afrikaans was not very good despite the lessons at school. But she knew Meneer Venter was swearing and that 'moer' was 'murder'. Who was he going to murder now? Was she not perhaps already standing on his wife?

The commotion got worse. She could hear sounds of running and other people coming outside. An elderly woman in housemaid's uniform hurried down steps from the stoep close by to Veronica, without noticing her huddled against the wall. She was moaning softly to herself. Meneer Venter was shouting about people who stole from him. Everyone would see now what he did to thieves.

Veronica was trembling but she had to find out what

was happening. She stretched forward to see around the corner. A small number of servants stood at a short distance from the massive figure – his face just a shade lighter than his blazing beard and hair. In front of him stood a black child with thin spindly legs, wearing a pair of torn khaki shorts, his eyes fixed on the ground. The man grabbed the boy's ear and jerked his head upwards, with his other hand forcing an orange into the boy's face. _Violent_

'Kyk hierso! Look at this! I'll teach you a lesson you'll never forget!' _lack of passion_

'Please Baas, this boy has learnt his lesson. He won't do it again Baas. I will speak to him Baas!'

It was the old housemaid, her hands together as if in a prayer, pleading, moving nearer to Meneer Venter. His arm swept out, dismissing her.

'He must learn a proper lesson. Talking is not good enough!'

The old woman was insistent. 'He's only a child my Baas. Once the Baas was also a child!'

Meneer Venter turned on her now. 'You go too far now Lettie. Watch out or I'll give you a lesson too!'

The old woman covered her face with her hands, shaking her head.

Meneer Venter shouted instructions to a couple of servants who disappeared through the side door. One came back with a wooden chair and the other with a cane. For a moment after his ear had been released, the boy looked around wildly. In the second that Veronica glimpsed his eyes, she almost called out. He looked like Selo, Rebecca's son, in the photograph! It couldn't be him, could it? Rebecca's family lived far away. But Rebecca had said Selo was always getting into trouble.

The boy was ordered to lean over the chair. One of

the male workers was ordered to stand in front and hold him down. Meneer Venter took the cane. Veronica did not look after the first two strikes. The boy's cries pierced her ears. She was shivering all over. Her stomach heaved.

When the cries reduced to a soft whimpering, Veronica looked up. To her horror Meneer Venter was walking in her direction in a slow swagger. There was no time and no where to run. Standing transfixed, she dropped the flower in her hand. His eyes were odd, glazed, as if not seeing anything. Then, as he drew close, they flickered.

'Jy is 'n van Reenen, ne? Tell your father I'm satisfied with the fence.'

Before Veronica could even think what to say, he patted her hair lightly and walked on, up the steps and into the house. He had thought she was Marika.

Guiltily, Veronica looked down at the fallen poinsettia. She was aware of the old woman gently holding the boy, making soothing noises. The small assembly of servants were talking quietly amongst themselves. Hastily she picked up the blood-red flower. The milky oozing had stopped and sealed up the stem. Grabbing a branch above her, she snapped off four more stems, careless of the sticky sap. A flower each. Sprinting down the road, she passed the old woman and the boy who had begun making their way painfully towards the huts behind the bluegums. No sounds followed as she entered the orange trees. She stopped running. She could walk the rest of the way now and give herself time to regain her breath. Then she could present each flower quite calmly. She might even take the gang some oranges.

77

# Robert and the Dog

by Ken Saro-Wiwa

Robert's new employer was a young medical doctor just returned from abroad. He was cheerful, exuberant and polite. It was obvious to Robert that he had not been in the country for a long time. Because he did not once lose his temper, he did not shout at Robert, he called him by his first name, and always asked him about his wife, children and other members of his family. Robert, accustomed to moving from household to household, thought he had at last found fulfilment. The more so as the young doctor appeared to be a bachelor.

Stewards, including Robert, prefer to serve a bachelor. Because every bachelor is as wax in the hands of his steward. The latter determines what is to be spent on grocery, how much food is to be served at meal times, what is to be done with the remnants of food. In short, he holds the bachelor's life in his hands. And that is tremendous power.

Robert quickly settled into his new situation and took full control of the house. Experience had taught him never to occupy the servants' quarters, which were attached to the main house. It made dismissals or the abandonment of a situation rather messy. So it was that Robert's family lived in the filth and quagmire of Ajegunle, which the wags termed 'The Jungle'. In his one-bedroom apartment in The Jungle, Robert was king. And he always repaired there nightly to exercise

78

his authority over his wife and six children. The experience he had gained in running his household helped him a great deal in organising the life of each new employer. Robert was particularly happy in his new situation because the young man was carefree and happy. There was, as has been said, no wife breathing down Robert's neck and limiting his abundant authority. There were no children whose nappies and numerous clothes had to be washed. He did not have to cook several meals a day. The young man ate but once a day, except for the cup of coffee and toast early in the morning.

Trouble began when the young man announced after six months that his wife was about to join him. Robert's face fell visibly at the announcement. But he did not worry very much at the expected curtailment of his wide powers. Who knew, the lady might not be an ogre after all.

Which is precisely what happened in the event. The lady was as young and cheerful as her husband. She, too, took an interest in Robert. She was European and excited about her first visit to Africa. She appeared pleased to have Robert's assistance. She spent the day asking Robert about African food, watching Robert at work in the kitchen and lending a helping hand where possible. She made sure Robert stopped work early so that he could get home to his family, and she did not make a fuss if Robert turned up late some odd mornings. And she got Robert paid every fortnight. She even offered to go and visit his wife and family in The Jungle. Robert carefully and politely turned down her offer. He could not imagine her picking her neat way through the filth and squalor of The Jungle to the hovel which was his home. Maybe, he thought, if she once knew where he lived and sampled the mess that was his home, her regard for him would diminish and he might lose his job. Yet the young lady extended every consideration to him. Robert began to feel like a human being, and he felt extremely grateful to his new employers.

The only source of worry in the new situation was the dog. For the young lady had arrived with a dog, called Bingo. And Robert watched with absolute amazement and great incredulity as the lady spoke tenderly to the dog. She ensured that he was well fed with tinned food and milk and meat and bones. And she held the dog lovingly in her arms, brushed his hair and tended him carefully. The dog appeared as important to the lady as her husband and, indeed, Robert thought, in the order of things, the dog was more important than himself. Try as hard as he might, he could not dismiss from his mind the fact that the dog was doing better than himself. And he detested this state of affairs. He could understand a dog being invited to eat up an infant's faeces. He could understand a stray, mangy dog with flies around its ears being beaten and chased away from the dwellings of men. He could understand a dog wandering around rubbish heaps in search of sustenance. But a dog who slept on the settee, a dog who was fed tinned food on a plate, a dog who was brushed and cleaned, a dog who drank good tinned milk, was entirely beyond his comprehension. On one occasion, the lady took the dog to a doctor. And that was the straw that broke the camel's back.

All that day, Robert felt his stomach turn. And when he got home in the evening and saw his children, with distended stomachs, gambolling in the filth that simmered in a swollen stream at his door, and watched them hungrily swallow small balls of *eba*, he asked himself, 'Who born dog?' And all of a sudden he developed a pathological hatred for Bingo the dog, his master's dog. All night long, he saw in the eye of his mind, the dog cuddled in the warmth of the settee, which he would have to clean and brush in the morning. And he asked himself again and again, 'Who born dog?'

The object of Robert's hatred was totally oblivious of the feelings that he bred in the cook-steward. He revelled in the love of his master and mistress. He ate his food with relish and wagged his tail in contented gratitude. He loved and served the lady, doing as he was bid. And he wagged his tail contentedly at Robert. He slept in the day and kept watch over his owners at night. But each wag of his tail was like so many pinpricks in the heart of Robert, who secretly vowed to 'show' the dog some day.

That day duly arrived and much sooner than Robert had expected. The young doctor announced to him that they would be going away on holiday for six weeks. He wanted Robert to take care of the house. As they would not be travelling with the dog, he would be most delighted if Robert would be kind enough to take care of Bingo. They were going to leave enough tinned food and milk for Bingo and some money so Robert could purchase bones to supplement his food. He hoped Robert did not mind.

Not in the least, Robert replied. But in his innermost heart, he knew he had found the opportunity he wanted.

After the departure of the couple, Robert, true to his training, obeyed his master's orders to the letter. On the first and second days. On the third day, watching the dog lap his milk from a plate, a voice spoke to Robert. 'Who born dog?' And to this

81

ponderous question, Robert could find no other
answer than 'Dog.' And the anger in him welled. He
looked at the dog, and the dog looked at him, wagging
his tail. 'Well may you wag your tail,' Robert thought,
'but I can tell you, I'm not going to waste my life taking
care of you.'

He gathered up all the tins of dog food, all the tins
of milk, tethered the dog to the settee and walked off,
out of the house and the job he had loved to do. He
gave the milk and dog food to his children when he got
home.

And the dog died.

82

# The Man

**by E. B. Dongala**

translated from French by Clive Wake

. . . No, this time he won't get away! After forty-eight hours, he had been tracked down, his itinerary was known and the village where he was hiding identified. But how many false leads there had been! He had been seen everywhere at once, as if he had the gift of ubiquity: dedicated militants had apparently run him down in the heart of the country without, however, managing to capture him: a patrol which had been parachuted into the northern swamps claimed they had badly wounded him, providing as their only proof traces of blood that disappeared into a ravine; frontier guards swore they had shot him in a canoe (which had unfortunately sunk) as he tried to escape by river: none of these claims survived closer investigation. The already tight police net was tightened still further, new brigades of gendarmes were created, and the army was given *carte blanche*. Soldiers invaded the working-class quarters of the city, breaking down the doors of houses, sticking bayonets into mattresses filled with grass and cotton, slashing open sacks of *foo-foo*, beating with their rifle butts anyone who didn't answer their questions quickly enough, or quite simply cutting down anyone who dared to protest at the violation of his home. But all these strong-arm tactics achieved nothing, and the country was on the verge of panic. Where could he be hiding?

It had been an almost impossible exploit, for the

*it seems as an attribute of God-like figure . . . ē tyrant is made fun of → seen as coward instead of brave figure.*

father-founder of the nation, the enlightened guide
and saviour of the people, the great helmsman, the
president-for-life, the commander-in-chief of the
armed forces and the beloved father of the people
lived in a vast palace out of bounds to the ordinary
citizen. In any case, the circular security system *irony: despite all this, ē ē man still found way in, so ur accept assassinated*
contrived by an Israeli professor with degrees in war
science and counter-terrorism was impregnable. Five
hundred yards from the palace perimeter, armed
soldiers stood guard at ten-yard intervals, day and
night, and this pattern was repeated at a distance of
two hundred and then one hundred yards from the
perimeter. The palace itself was also surrounded by a
water-filled moat of immense depth swarming with
African and Indian crocodiles and caymans imported
from Central America which most certainly didn't feed
solely on small fry, especially during the campaigns of
repression that regularly fell upon the country after
every genuine or mock *coup d'état*. Behind the moat was
a ditch full of black mambas and green mambas whose
powerful venom killed their victims on the spot. The
perimeter wall itself – an enormous sixty-foot high
structure of brick and stone as imposing as the wall of
the Zimbabwe ruins – bristled with watchtowers,
search-lights, nails, barbed wire and broken glass;
access was by two enormous doors which also served as
a drawbridge and were controlled from the inside
alone. Finally the palace itself, the holy of holies, where
the beloved father of the people lived: one hundred
and fifty rooms in which scores of huge mirrors
reflected everything and everyone, multiplying and
reducing them *ad infinitum*, so that visitors always felt
uneasy and oppressed, aware that their least gestures
were being watched. Every movement, however small,
was carried like an echo from room to room, from

mirror to mirror, until it reached the ultimate mirror of all, the eye of the master himself, watching over that entire universe. No one knew in which room the founder-president slept, not even the well-versed prostitutes he employed for several nights at a stretch for his highly sophisticated pleasures; even less likely to know were the unspoilt, happy little girls he enjoyed deflowering between the promulgation of two decrees from his palace of wonders. But, if the beloved-father-of-the-nation-the-supreme-and-enlightened-guide-the-commander-in-chief-of-the-armed-forces-and-beneficent-genius-of-mankind was invisible in the flesh to the majority of his subjects, he was, on the other hand, everywhere present: it was a statutory requirement that his portrait should hang in all homes. The news bulletins on the radio always began and ended with one of his stirring thoughts. The television news began, continued and finished in front of his picture, and the solitary local newspaper published in every issue at least four pages of letters in which citizens proclaimed their undying affection. Everywhere present but inaccessible. That was why the exploit was impossible.

And yet he had carried it off: he had succeeded in getting into the palace, bypassing the crocodiles, the mambas and the Praetorian guards; he had succeeded in outwitting the trap of the mirrors and had executed the father of the nation as one kills a common agitator and fomenter of coups. And then he had made the return journey, avoiding the watchtowers, the drawbridge, the green mambas, the black mambas, the crocodiles, and the Praetorian guards. And escaped! Forty-eight hours later he was still free!

. . . And then came the rumour, no one knew where from: he had been tracked down, his itinerary was known, and the village where he was hiding had been identified; he was surrounded. This time he wouldn't get away!

Armoured cars, jeeps, and lorries full of soldiers set off at three in the morning. The tanks didn't trouble to go round the houses in the villages through which they passed, a straight line being the shortest distance between two points: villages were left burning behind them, crops were laid waste, corpses piled up in the furrows made by their caterpillar tracks. Conquerors indeed in a defeated country, they soon reached their destination. They woke up the villagers with their rifle butts. They searched everywhere, emptied the granaries, looked in the trees and inside lofts. They didn't find the man they were looking for. The officer in command of the soldiers was furious, and his neck seemed to explode under his chinstrap:

'I know he's here, the bastard who dared to murder our dear beloved founder-president who will live for ever in the pantheon of our immortal heroes. I know the miserable wretch has a beard and is blind in one eye. If you don't tell me within ten minutes where he's hiding, I'll burn all your houses, I'll take one of you at random and have him tortured and shot!'

The ten minutes passed amid a frightened silence as deep as the silence that preceded the creation of the world. Then the officer in command of the soldiers ordered the reprisals to begin. They man-handled the villagers: some were strung up by their feet and beaten; others had red pimento rubbed into their open wounds; yet others were forced to eat fresh cow dung . . . The villagers didn't denounce the hunted man. So they burned all the houses in the village, and the harvest as well, the fruits of a year's labour in a country where people rarely have enough to eat. The villagers still didn't give them the information they were seeking. In fact, the reason for their silence was quite simple: they genuinely did not know who had carried out the deed.

The man had acted alone. He had spent months making his preparations, reading, studying, planning; then he had put on a false beard and covered his left eye with a black band, like a pirate. He had found how to penetrate the impregnable palace and kill the great dictator; the way he had done it was so simple he had sworn to himself that he would never reveal it, even under torture, for it could be used again. He was nevertheless surprised to see the soldiers in his village. But had they really discovered his identity or were they just bluffing? Clearly, they didn't know who he was, standing there in front of them, among his fellow villagers who were themselves in total ignorance of what he had done. There he stood, clean-shaven and with both his eyes, waiting to see what would happen next.

The officer in charge of the soldiers, a commandant, got angrier still, confronted by his victims' silence:

'I repeat for the last time! If you do not tell me where he is hiding, this bastard one-eyed son-of-a-whore without balls who has murdered our beloved president-for-life, founder of our party and leader of the nation, I'll take one of you at random and shoot him! I'll give you five minutes!'

He looked feverishly at his quartz watch. Two minutes. One minute. Thirty seconds.

'I assure you, commandant,' the village chief pleaded, 'we don't know him and we assure you he isn't in our village.'

'Too bad for you. I'm going to take a man at random and shoot him in front of you all. That will perhaps help you to understand. You, there!'

The commandant was pointing at him. He wasn't even surprised, as if he had always expected it. Deep down, it was what he wanted, for he doubted that he would be able to go through the rest of his life with an easy conscience if he allowed someone else to die in his place. He was pleased, for he would have the satisfaction of dying with his secret.

'You will be the innocent hostage who has to be sacrificed because of the obstinacy of your chief and your fellow villagers. Tie him to a tree and shoot him!'

They kicked him and beat him with rifle butts, they slashed him with bayonets. He was dragged along the ground and tied to a mango tree. His wife flung herself on him, to be brutally pulled away. Four soldiers took aim.

'One last time, tell us where the murderer is hiding.'

'I don't know, commandant!' pleaded the chief.

'Fire!'

His chest jerked forward slightly, then he collapsed without a sound. They would never find him now!

The smoke cleared. The villagers remained plunged in a deep, stunned, silence, looking at the body slumped in the coarse liana ropes. The commandant, having carried out his threat, stood before them. He hesitated, not quite sure what to threaten them with now. Overcome by an inner panic, he struggled, at least to preserve the honour of his stripes.

'Well?' he asked.

At last the villagers became aware of him again.

'Well what!' roared the chief angrily. 'I told you we didn't know the man you're looking for. You didn't believe us and now you have killed one of us. What more can I say!'

The commandant could find nothing by way of reply. He rocked on his feet, uncertain what to do next, and at last called out an order to his men:

'Attention! Form up! The hunt goes on. The bastard may be hiding in the next village. There's no time to waste. Forward march!'

Then, turning to the villagers, he screamed: 'We'll find him, the son of a bastard, we'll flush him out wherever he's hiding, we'll pull off his balls and his ears, we'll pull out his nails and his eyes, we'll hang him naked in public in front of his wife, his mother and his children, and then we'll feed him to the dogs. You have my word on that.'

The jeeps and the tanks moved off and went elsewhere in search of 'the man'.

They are still looking for him. They sense his presence; somewhere he is hiding, but where? Crushed by dictatorship, the people feel their hearts beat faster when there is talk of 'the man'. Although the country is more police-ridden than ever, although it is crawling with spies, informers and hired killers, and although he has appointed as heads of security men from his own tribe entirely loyal to his cause, the new president, the second beloved father of the nation, entrusted with the task of continuing the sacred work of the father-founder, no longer dares go out. In order to frustrate the spell, he has issued a decree proclaiming himself unkillable and immortal, but still he hides away in the depths of his palace, with its labyrinth of passages and corridors, mirrors and reflections, walled up because he doesn't know when 'the man' will suddenly appear to strike him down in his turn, so that freedom, too long suppressed, may at last burst forth.

'The man', the hope of a nation and a people that says NO, and watches . . . .

89

*[handwritten at top: My analysis 4 "Why Apes Look like Ppl".]*

- ## Focus on language

*[handwritten: – Use of details; – animals caressed a lot with each other]*

# Why Apes Look Like People

*[handwritten: God – parody of authority; – God made man in his likeness.]*

**by Julius Lester**

*[handwritten: contentment + acceptance]*

For a long time after the Lord created the world, the only creatures on it were the animals. They swam the rivers, climbed the mountains, flew through the air, and lived their lives. They learned who to fear and who to greet as a friend, and they followed the fortunes and misfortunes of the seasons and the years, each day flowing from the one previous and toward the one to come.

*[handwritten margin: Deer has many; – Sense of contentment hierarchy; upset by appearance of man; brought chaos + pain.]*

*[handwritten: interrupts ē routine (diff. day)]*

One day, the Deer family was drinking at the lake at that time of the day when the sun seems to stop at the top of the sky. Suddenly, a loud noise caused the air to tremble, and the youngest Deer fell at the water's edge, a trickle of blood coming from its side. Frightened, the other Deer ran to the safety of the woods, except for the oldest child. He, too, was frightened, but his curiosity was so strong that he returned to the edge of the forest, and there hid behind a tree to see if the loud noise was going to be repeated or if anything else were going to happen.

*[handwritten: – Sense of hierarchy very human.]*
*[handwritten: not generel, rep. own species.]*

He had scarcely hidden himself when an animal he had never seen came down to the lakeside. It was a horrible-looking creature. It walked on two legs and

*[handwritten: grotesque des.; → foreshadow Mans horrible acts.]*

had no hair except for a little on its small, round head. The Deer had never heard of such an animal. He couldn't even remember his cousin, the Moose, ever talking about such an animal and the Moose would surely have seen such a creature, for he often went up into the high mountains and had seen many strange things.

The creature carried a long piece of wood in one of its paws. It stooped down, lay the piece of wood to one side, and magically began taking the skin off his younger brother with something it clutched in its paw. The Deer's fright became stronger than his curiosity, and he turned and bolted through the forest to tell his father what he had seen.

The father found it hard to believe what his oldest son told him. He had lived a long time, had talked to many animals, and had been many places. He had never heard of any creature such as this.

The next day, however, the father repeated the story to every animal he met. None of them had heard of such an animal, either. Several weeks passed. The Deer family found a new lake to drink from, and they had almost put the incident out of their minds, when, late one afternoon, while resting in a grove of shady trees, the father overheard two birds talking.

'Did you hear what happened this morning?'

'You mean about the Robin family?' the second bird responded.

'Yes.'

'Everybody's been talking about it. One of the Robins was flying home after spending the morning with a sick relative, I heard. Suddenly there was a loud noise, and he fell out of the sky like a dead limb dropping from a tree.'

'That's exactly what I heard,' the first bird said.

*minds also embody Man's aspects,*
*rationalize*

*exhibit Man's attributes, qualities.*

'What do you think happened?'

*(1-to Man to try to find*
*possible explan³ things they don't understood.*

'Well, it sounds to me like he had a sudden attack of some sort. You know, this time of year you have to be careful just what kind of worms you eat. He could've eaten some bad worms, and that could've caused a sudden attack of some kind.'

'Maybe so, but I've never heard of anything like that happening before.'

'Well, that's true.'

'And I heard that after the loud noise, he started bleeding.'

'Bleeding!'

The father Deer could contain himself no longer, and he excitedly told the birds what had happened to his youngest child. He described the strange animal his oldest son had seen, but the birds could give him no clue as to what it might be. They promised, however, to keep a sharp eye out for such a creature. They covered many miles in the course of a day and saw many things. In fact, they told him that they would give the description to all the other birds and, without a doubt, if such a creature really existed, one of the birds would see him sooner or later.

Hardly a day had passed when the Hawk happened to see just such an animal near the lake where the young Deer had been killed. The Hawk wanted to get a closer look at the creature, and, although the Hawk knew what had happened to the young Deer and the bird, the Hawk knows no fear. So he folded back his wings and dropped from the sky into a tall tree from which he could observe the new animal.

He watched the animal most of the day and saw it take wood and create a fire. This creature could do what the lightning could do when it struck a tree during a storm. The creature then took a large piece of

*Similarities w/ mans animal?*
*differences are apparent.*

*é robin? Suggest wanton killing.*

meat and placed it on the wood, which was turning black. After the meat had turned black, the creature took it out of the fire and began eating it. The Hawk had seen enough, and, spreading his great wings, he went to tell others what he had seen.

By this time, other animals in other parts of the forest had begun to tell stories about a creature who walked on two legs and had no hair, and when the news brought by the Hawk began to spread, no one doubted any longer that a new animal was living among them.

For many days, the animals talked among themselves, wondering what kind of animal it was that talked to no other animal and considered all animals its enemy. Finally, the Rabbit sent word through the forest that all the animals shoud send a representative to a meeting to discuss the situation. The other animals agreed that the Rabbit always did have good ideas, and the next evening, as the sun was setting, a group of them met in the deepest part of the forest.

'Well, I think everybody knows why we're here,' the Rabbit began. 'Anybody have any ideas?'

There was a long silence. Finally, the Frog spoke. 'Well, Mr Rabbit, we never had a problem like this.'

*black language*

'That's right,' the Elephant added. 'This new animal don't obey no rules. There doesn't seem to be anybody he likes.'

The other animals muttered in agreement, but no one had any suggestions. They thought for a long while. 'Mr Rabbit?' the Snake asked. 'You're a better talker than the rest of us. Maybe if you went and talked to him and explained to him how things are, you know, maybe he'd change his ways.'

'That's not a bad idea,' the Mouse added.

'He *is* new around here,' the Fish commented. 'He probably just doesn't know any better.'

All the animals thought it was a good idea, so early the next morning the Rabbit went down to the lake to talk to the new animal and explain to him all the rules and regulations they'd worked out for living with one another. Unknown to the Rabbit, the Hawk, high in the sky, had decided to follow him. The Hawk didn't like the Rabbit, but he still didn't like the idea of the Rabbit going to meet the new animal alone. He thought all of the animals had to protect each other until they learned who and what this new animal was. After that, they could go back to doing as they pleased.

The Rabbit hadn't been at the lake for more than a few minutes when he saw the new animal. He hopped over to him, and, before he could get a word out of his mouth, the creature snatched him up into its arms. The Rabbit tried to squirm away, but the creature squeezed him tighter.

With his keen eyes, the Hawk saw everything, and he fell, like bolt of lightning, to the earth. As he neared the strange creature, he gave a loud shriek, stretched his legs, bared his talons, and dug them into the creature's shoulders. The creature screamed and dropped the Rabbit. The Hawk picked the Rabbit up quickly, remembering not to dig his talons too deeply into the Rabbit's body, and was back into the upper reaches of the sky before the creature's screams had died.

That night, the animals held another meeting at which the Rabbit and the Hawk reported what had happened. The animals quickly concluded that they couldn't risk sending anyone else to hold a conference with the new animal.

'So what do we do now?' the Deer asked.

'Kill him!' the Rabbit exclaimed. 'Mr Lion. You're always roaring like you're the baddest thing around.

You go get him.'

The Lion shook his head. 'One of my cousins tried to fight him, and the creature has a stick that spits fire and kills. That's how my cousin was killed. Seems to me that Mr Hawk did a pretty good job of saving your life today.'

'Yeah, Mr Hawk. What about you?' the other animals asked all at once. 'You can do it.'

The Hawk thought it over for a while. He didn't like the idea. He much preferred soaring in the upper reaches of the air away from everyone. He really didn't like being around other animals or even being too close to the ground. In fact, if he could've had his way, there would've been food in the air for him to eat so that the only part of the earth he'd ever have to touch would be the top of a mountain. Once or twice a week he was able to snatch a bird out of the air, but too often he had to come right down to the ground to get food, and he didn't like it too much. So he declined. He'd done all he was going to do. Somebody else had to do something now.

The other animals were angry, but the Hawk wouldn't change his mind. The animals continued to argue with him, and, after a few minutes, he simply spread his wings and, sending a cool breeze over them, he flew back to where the clouds lived.

The animals spent a good hour cussing the Hawk before they calmed down enough to continue with the meeting. After several hours, they decided that part of their problem was that they didn't know what kind of animal it was. If they knew that, it might give them some idea what to do. So they decided that the next morning the Rabbit, the Deer, and the Frog would go up to Heaven to see God. If anybody knew, God had to know.

It was late morning when they got to Heaven, but God was just waking up, and he couldn't see them until he had finished his coffee. The Lord gets kind of grouchy if he doesn't have a cup of coffee in the morning, so they sat on the porch and waited.

Finally, the Lord came out. 'Well, well, well,' he said, sitting down in his rocking chair. 'It's been a long time since any of you have been up here. Must be something wrong.' He chuckled.

'I think the last time you brought a delegation up here, Mr Rabbit, was when you got that petition together asking me to stop wintertime.'

The Rabbit smiled sheepishly. 'Well, I've gotten used to that, Lord.'

'Didn't I tell you you would? I hope everything's all right now.'

'Well, Lord, to tell you the truth, everything's not all right.'

'What's the matter? You got plenty of water don't you?'

'Water's fine, Lord, but—'

'Plenty tree-leaves to munch on for snacks?'

'Plenty tree-leaves, Lord. The thing is—'

'Ain't there enough oxygen in the air? I'll have to admit that it took me a while to find just the right amount of oxygen to put in the air, but it's O.K. now, ain't it?'

'Couldn't be better, Lord, but—'

'And I shortened the nights like you asked me to. I just can't see what's wrong this time, Mr Rabbit.'

'Well, Lord, if you'd hush up, I'd tell you!'

'Now just slow down a minute, Mr Rabbit. I'm just trying to see if my world is functioning all right. First world I ever made, you know, and it wasn't no easy job.'

'We understand that, Lord,' the Deer said.

'Yes, Lord. We understand that,' the Rabbit repeated. 'And we think you did a fine job, considering how you're an amateur and all that. However, there's a new animal down there.'

'Oh! You must mean Man!' the Lord interrupted.

'Man?'

'Uh-huh. An animal that walks on two legs.'

'And <u>ain</u>'t got no hair?' the Deer wanted to know.

'That's him,' the Lord said. 'And let me tell you, it was a hard job putting him together. I remember I started early one Monday morning. I'd had the idea tucked away in my head for a long time, so I figured it wouldn't take me more than a few hours to put him together. Well, let me tell you, Mr Rabbit—'

'Uh, Lord. We understand. We'd like to hear about it, but we just don't have the time today, Lord. While we're up here talking with you, that man-animal is down there killing everything he can get his hands on.'

'What was that?'

'That's the truth, Lord. Now you know how we got things worked out among ourselves, so that the deer know to stay away from the lions, and the ground hog looks out for the snake and the fish try to stay out of the bear's way. It's a pretty good arrangement. We don't have to walk around being afraid of everybody else. But this man-animal!' And the Rabbit, the Deer, and the Frog took turns telling God the entire story.

After they finished, the Lord didn't say anything for a long while. He stared off into space and looked very sad. 'Well,' he said finally, 'I think everything will work out all right. I thought man might have a little trouble getting adjusted to everything, but you take my word for it, everything'll be O.K.'

The Rabbit, the Deer, and the Frog expressed some doubts, but after God reassured them several times,

*evidence of how man destroys to native*

they went back and reported to the other animals. Things didn't get better, though. More and more of the man-animals began to appear in the forest, and one evening the birds came home to find that some trees had been cut down, including the one they lived in. Soon the man-animals had cleared a lot of the forest, and the animals moved to another forest. It wasn't long, though, before the man-animals came to that forest and cut it down, and the animals had to move again.

Everywhere the animals lived, the man-animals came. They put aeroplanes in the air, and the Hawk was sorry that he had not tried to kill the man-animal when he had the chance. They put boats on the water and submarines in the sea. They built roads through the middle of mountains and laid pipes deep in the ground, and the ground hogs and all their relatives had to move. They built cities beside rivers and poured gallons of foul liquids into the rivers, and many fish died. The smoke from their cities filled the air, and no birds could live in the cities. They sprayed plants with liquids, and many animals died because there were no clean plants to eat.

The animals moved to new forests, but the man-animal was never far behind. Finally, the animals were tired of moving. Once again, the Rabbit called a meeting and all the animals came, even the Hawk.

They talked about it for several days. The Bear suggested that they make war on the man-animals, but, after much discussion, they couldn't figure how they could get guns and tanks and aeroplanes. Eventually, the Owl, who was the wisest of the animals, said, 'The only sensible thing we can do is to become man-animals ourselves. That is the only way we will ever be as powerful as they are.'

*realised their own limitations.*
*can't beat em, join en.*
*∴ Sad irony*

*Signi. of lord*
*creates Man*
*destroys, behind it all.*

'You're right!' the Rabbit exclaimed instantly.

The other animals agreed, and they quickly formed a delegation to go tell God the news.

When they got to Heaven the next morning, the Lord had already finished his morning coffee and was sitting on the porch reading the paper. 'Well,' he said, putting the paper down. 'How y'all doing?'

'Lord, you got to turn us into man-animals,' the Rabbit said immediately. He didn't have time for a whole lot of chit-chat that morning.

'Do what?'

'That's right, Lord. That's the only way we can be as powerful as man-animal is and protect ourselves. Otherwise, we don't stand a chance.'

The Lord thought it over for a long while. He didn't want to do it, but things hadn't worked out with man-animal as well as he had hoped. In fact, things had turned out pretty bad. Something should've told him that it was going to turn out that way because he'd had such problems making man-animal. Well, win a few and lose a few, thought the Lord. 'O.K., animals. Tomorrow morning there'll be a big pot of oil in the middle of the forest. Every animal who washes himself in that oil will become a man-animal.'

The animals cheered and rushed back to tell the others. And when they heard the news, they were delirious with joy.

'When I get to be a man-animal,' said the Bear, 'I'm gon' get me a car. A red convertible with white seats. Tell me I ain't gon' be tough!'

'Wait'll you see me in one of them continental suits!' the Rabbit exclaimed. 'Won't be nobody as dap as me nowhere. All them women gon' look at me and say, "Who is that fine young daddy?"'

All night long the animals stayed up talking about

99

what they were going to do when they became people. Some had already decided that they were going to form a company to buy land, because if anybody knew what land had oil and gold and silver and everything else on it, they sure did. The Jaguar was already campaigning among the other animals to vote for him for President.

They were making so much noise that the Lord couldn't help but hear them. He listened for a while and became very sad. He couldn't help but think that if they were acting this way now, he didn't want to imagine how they would act when they became people. And the world was in bad enough shape as it was. He was so depressed about it that he was thinking of going off and building another world. And as he listened to the animals talk about what they were going to do when they became people, he decided that the last thing the world needed was any more people. *Sad thing*

So he threw a thunderbolt down from Heaven and broke the pot of oil, and when the animals came upon it the next morning, there were just a few drops left in some of the cracked pieces, and while the other animals were looking at it in shock and amazement, the Ape, the Gorilla, the Chimpanzee, and the Monkey rushed over and washed their faces, hands, and feet in the few drops that remained. And that's why those animals look like people. *fable ends on a humorous note that chimps gorilla, apes, monkeys look like man but sends negative vibes — that amongst God's all creatures, Man is the worst & possibly a mistake.* comic note *manages in this fable.*

# Full Stop

**by Alecia McKenzie**

My grandmother writes without commas or full stops
She writes My Dear Carmen Greetings in Jesus
Precious name Its so nice hearing from you The time
doesnt matter as long as we are in each others thoughts
Well Im here still holding on praying for a better way
of living myself We just have to keep hoping that our
sweet Saviour helps us take each day one at a time We
know not what the future holds but we sure know who
holds the key and its a secret to him only so we just
have to keep praying to him Thanks very much for
your letters and money You are in my thoughts all
along the way My knees are very weak now Old age is
on me now I have somebody to take me to church and
back Thank God for that Give regards to your hubby
for me until I know him to do so myself So keep sweet
as always Cherio for now and God Bless Same old
Grand Ma Scottie PS write your mother

And I write back saying Grandma what do you mean
by God bless And whats this about weak knees You
know youre fit as a fiddle Dont let anybody fool you
that 73 is old Normy is fine and he sends you his love
Enclosed is $75 Take care of yourself and I hope to be
home one of these days Love Carmen

She writes back saying Dear Carmen I got your letter
yesterday Why are you writing me without punctuation
Dont you know better Is that what I worked hard and
sent you to school for Dont let me down like this

Thanks for the money It came just in time to buy some paint for the old shack here But its not enough to pay for a painter so Im going to do the job myself with Gods help I pray for you every night that you stay healthy and good I truly hope you make it home for Christmas at least Love to your hubby God Bless and write your mother Same Grand Ma Scottie

Dear Grandma,

Please don't go painting at your age. Enclosed is $100 to pay a painter. Remember the last time you painted the house you fell off the ladder? God didn't catch you then, and you spent weeks in the hospital and hated it. Please get someone. Normy sends his love.
Love,
Carmen

Dear Carmen God bless you for the money I put it in the bank You think Im too old to paint my own house The painters on this island are all thieves They charge you a cow and a horse and when theyre done you have to do it over Its better to do the job yourself from the start Child I heard from your mother the other day Shes now in London She wrote that the man shes now living with is working as a hotel doorman and that he really loves his uniform The damn fools She didnt ask a word about how I was doing and she didnt even send a red cent But you cant expect such people to change She said she wrote you many times and you havent replied You should write her She is still your mother Our Saviour says to forgive and forget I must leave you now in the hands of him from whom all blessings flow So keep sweet and take care Yours the same Grand Ma PS Dont make jokes about God not catching me You know better Write your mother and say hello to your hubby

Dear Grandma,

Sorry to take so long to write but I just changed jobs. I'm working at a bigger hospital now, but I'm on the night shift so it's hard to get time to sit down and do anything.

I'm sorry, but every time I try to write my 'mother', no words come. What do you say to somebody you've seen only once? As far as I'm concerned the person who raised me is my mother, and that's you.

I'm glad you managed to paint the house but please don't do it again. Old bones break easily, you know (smile). Enclosed is $75. Normy sends his love.

Love,

Carmen

My Dear Carmen Suppose our Saviour was to say that since Joseph raised him God is not his father Wouldnt God be upset Same for your mother You came from her and nothing can change that Forgive 7 times 7 our Good Lord said Thanks for the money I put half of it in the bank Your brother never writes not a line but Im used to it When last did you hear from him My love things on the island are getting worse but Im too old to move now The thieves are breaking into everybodys house but I suppose its the same in New York The Sweet Lord has spared my old shack But let anyone try to break in and see if I dont chop him up with this machete I keep under my bed Take care of yourself and say hello to hubby Remember to pray Write to your mother She would love to hear from you Same Grand Ma Scottie

Dear Grandma,

Enclosed is $200. Get somebody to put burglar bars over all the windows. Why don't you rent out one of the rooms so that at least you won't be alone in the house at nights?

I got another letter from my 'mother', saying she would love me to come over to England for a holiday. What would I do in England? With the little holidays I get, I'd rather come back home. Besides what would we have to talk about? She's almost a complete stranger to me.

I'm now on the day shift, by the way, which gives me a bit more time to myself in the evenings. Normy is fine. Maybe you'll even have a great-grandchild soon. We're thinking about it.

Love,

Carmen

P.S. Richie called me a few days ago. He says he'll write soon.

Dear Carmen You shouldnt talk that way about your mother She was young when she had you and didnt know better I was the one who told her to let me raise you so that she could go to England for a better life for herself When she brought me Richie two years later that was a different story But the good Lord knows best Dont hold it against her Forgive us our sins as we forgive them that sin against us Her problem is that she was born a fool when it comes to men but not everybody can be smart Thank God for your brains my child I always knew you would be a lawyer doctor or Indian Chief ha ha ha I pray for you Thanks for the money you sent I bought a new mattress because the old one was really getting too soft You wouldn't believe the price of mattresses on this island these days I dont know how poor people manage But the Good Lord dont give us more than we can bear Say hello to your hubby and stop thinking about the baby and have it

Youll soon be thirty and then youll have a really tough time Same Grand Ma Scottie PS I dont want anybody living with me in the house The people on this island will rob you blind And I dont like burglar bars God will protect me from evil

Dear Grandma,

You shouldn't rely too much on God these days. Please put up some burglar bars. I'm sending the money for it.

The job at the hospital is very stressful, especially when you're on emergency. You wouldn't believe the things people do to one another in New York. Believe me, you're much better off on the island.

By the way, I got a letter from your daughter the same day your letter came. She says she has a cyst in one eye and has to be operated on. She asked me what she should do, as if I'm an eye specialist. She also said she wants to come to New York for the operation. Don't they have plenty doctors in England? I wish she would leave me alone. Let her go to California where Richie is if she wants to do the operation in the States.

By the way, Normy and I have decided we're too busy now for children. So we've put it off for another couple of years. Lots of people have children when they're in their thirties without any problems. Don't be disappointed.
Love,
Carmen

My Dear Carmen Whats wrong with you The Lord said be fruitful and multiply Stop wasting time I would like to see your children before Our Saviour calls me onto him Keep that in mind Your mother wrote me too about the cyst I feel sorry for her but the Lord gives and the Lord takes away Maybe you should let her come and stay with you for just a little while Mr Bax up the road died last week and since I didnt have a thing to wear to the funeral I bought a dress with the money you sent The burglar bars will come another time It was a lovely funeral Everybody turned out We sang Closer My God To Thee Miss Gerdy told me I still have a good voice Did you know that I sang in a choir when I was younger Your mother did too before she met the no good boy your father I forget his name May he rest in peace Its a wonderful thing to give praise onto the Lord I hope youre still saying your prayers Kiss hubby for me and write your mother Same Grand Ma Scottie

Dear Grandma,

Sorry to hear about Mr Bax. He was a nice man. Remember how he always brought me and Richie mangoes from his Bombay tree?

By the way, did you give your daughter my telephone number? She called and said she's definitely coming to New York for the operation. I didn't even recognise her voice until she told me who she was. I'm sure I wouldn't recognise her if I saw her on the street. She says she isn't asking me to put her up, that she'll stay at a hotel. I hope she's already reserved a room because I don't have time for any foolishness.

Did you get a letter from Richie now? He phoned me not too long ago, said he got promoted to assistant manager at his job. He said he sent you some money for your birthday. Did you get my card?

Take care and write soon. Normy sends his love.
Love,
Carmen

My Dear Carmen I didnt get any letter from your

brother Ask him if he remembered to post it Thanks for your card and the gift inside I put it in the bank When the Lord calls me this money will all come back to you because he that giveth shall receiveth and you have given me a lot in these years You have given me a lot of joy no matter what your mother may tell you Are you sure she is coming to America Child be careful of her for she is a snake in the grass But still she is your mother and Our Saviour says honour thy father and mother Im feeling very old these days and I would like to see you and get to know my grand son in law before He gathers me onto his bosom Write soon and be nice to your mother when she comes even though it will be hard Same Grand Ma Scottie

Dear Grandma,

Well, she showed up. Unfortunately I wasn't at home at the time so Normy let her in. I almost had a heart attack when I got home and saw her. She looks much younger than 47 and she was dressed to match. She brought us lots of presents – bedspreads, tablecloths and all that old British stuff. She acted as if I was her long lost baby. Do you know what she said? She said that she and my father made an agreement with you and that you broke it. She said that because they didn't have any money when I was born they asked you to keep me for a while. Then they went to England because there were jobs there. But soon she got pregnant with Richie and had to bring him to you as well. She said that when I was six and Richie was four, Daddy was killed on a construction site. She said that afterwards she came back for us and you refused to give us up. You hid us with your relatives in St Thomas, she said. She also said that you hated Daddy from the start because he wouldn't go to church. I don't believe her but she swears it's true. She cried the whole night. Please tell me what really happened. I wish she hadn't come.

Love,

Carmen

My Dear Carmen Your mother was always a snake in the grass Dont believe a word she says She and your father were not fit to raise you so The Good Lord appointed me guardian He did not want you to be raised in England so he gave you onto my care And look how fine youve turned out

Well I finally got a letter from Richard He said he couldnt write before because he was working overtime he moved into a new appartment and horse dead and cow fat Excuses and more excuses When are you coming home I don't 'have much longer on this earth you know I can hardly put one foot in front of the other these days Pray for me The thieves on the island are getting really bold On Tuesday night they broke into Miss Gerdys house although she has at least five dogs A mangy lot They took everything they could lay their hands on and she slept right through it Never heard a thing she said the next morning Im going to put up the burglar bars after all My dear remember the ten commandments and keep good and strong Kiss your hubby for me and tell your mother God bless Same Grand Ma Scottie

# The Escape

**by Millie Murray**

'Who put de clock back, eh!!'

Silence. 'Who put de clock back? If me have fi lick every one of yu pickney dis day, eh . . .' Daddy looked into four pairs of eyes, each eye running water, set into four heads shaking from side to side in denial of the crime, four snivelling noses, four pairs of trembling lips, with slightly audible sounds escaping, but not enough to call attention to the owner.

'Not me, Daddy,' chorused four voices in unison. 'All right, me have fi beat yu all one by one fi find out de truth den.' Daddy was a tall man. Well, he was tall to us kids. He was a red colour. In fact, he was part Arawak Indian. He had silky hair which he used to shine up with Dixie Peach hair rubbing. He was quite stocky, and his hands had a large span. When they made contact with any part of your skin, boy, you could feel it.

A chorus of voices wailing and shrieking into a loud crescendo. The joke was nobody had got beaten yet! 'Me can't imagine how yuh mudder gone, gone leave me wid de pickney dem, bout she gone to see her mudder,' Daddy said in an incredulous voice. 'An me a tink seh is only nine in a de morning, and is twelve o'clock an I late for work.'

You can't blame my mother for taking off. She never deserted us completely. We all knew that she was coming back to us. If Daddy had been a reasonable

109

man, he would have been happy for her to go home to see her mother. But he wasn't. Mummy had to sneak out like a child who is in fear of her father. My mother had been in Britain for twenty-one years and had never in all that time returned to Jamaica to see her family because my father would not let her. Mind you, he had been to see his family. When I think about it my father was an out-and-out bully. All my mother ever said was that she wanted a quiet life, so he used to abuse her, especially mentally, and she would let him get away with it. He would argue and want to start a fight. My mother would calmly ignore him, which in fact angered him more. He was a bit of a womaniser, and my mother was a generous-looking woman, which I think provoked my father's feelings of jealousy. And what with his guilty conscience about whatever he was up to at the time, he was totally unreasonable. 'Yu a get feisty, yu want come out and find work,' he would say to her on Fridays, after reluctantly giving her a pittance for housekeeping for the week.

I loved my father, but I preferred my mother. I loved her best. She was so understanding, you could talk to her about most things. She was quite a liberal woman, especially in those days of West Indian parents who had old values, and there were certain things you couldn't tell even your mother!

'My!! Me have fi pay de gas bill, de light bill, de telephone bill,' he would moan, on and on. One day I said, 'Daddy, you always say you have to pay the telephone bill, but we haven't got a telephone have we?' Bof! Slap! Tump! Skin contacting skin. Daddy's hand on my legs. 'Who ask yu fi fast in big people business,' was my answer from Daddy. 'Yu pickney a born inna Britain too feisty fi yu own good.'

My mother was beginning to feel desperate. She

badly wanted to see her mother, who was quite old and had hypertension, and my mother's fear was that her mother would die before she had a chance to see her again. It was very sad. Us children would feel at a loss as to what we could do. It was horrible seeing your mother pine away quietly. She would be doing some washing in the kitchen, and then she would look up out of the window and you could feel vibes generating from her, from her yearning to go home to Jamaica. And she would be transfixed, deep in her own thoughts about her life that she had left behind. She would say, 'De sky at home is so different, clear, blue an warm,' and she would tell us stories of when she was a child, and the things that she used to get up to. She would make us laugh with little rhymes she would repeat time and time again for us.

Mummy had a friend called Miz Ruby. She was deadly. She couldn't stand my father. He couldn't stand her. 'Dat woman just a look fi man, before she go home an stop fast inna people business,' he would tell my mother. 'Yu tell her fi her face, if yu nar want her fi come an see me,' my mother would say to him. But for some unknown reason my father never seemed to have the courage to say anything to Miz Ruby, which at the time I could not understand.

'Evenin', Miz Ruby,' he would grunt under his breath. 'Evenin',' Miz Ruby would say as she waltzed past him in the passage. 'Hello, Patsy,' she would say to my mother with a smile on her face, rolling her eyes back to indicate the contempt that she felt for my father. My mother would just smile back, and say 'How yu bin,' sweetly to Miz Ruby, and they would both laugh as though they had just heard a huge joke.

Miz Ruby was a big brown-skinned woman. She had incredibly large breasts. I used to wonder how she managed to walk around with them all day. In fact all of her was large. She was indeed a jovial person, always laughing. She even had a kind word to say to us kids, which was unusual, for a big person to acknowledge children then. She always brought coconut cake for us, which she had made herself. It was rock hard and sweet, and we had to dig out the coconut from our teeth. She never had anything good to say about Daddy. 'Miserable ole goat,' she would say indignantly. 'Patsy me tell yu all de time, if yu want fi borrow money fi go home, just ask fi me an I will draw my pardner money fi give yu.'

'No. It all right Miz Ruby, me piece a money a week time me get inna de factory will cover. Me have everyting sort out, no worry,' Mummy would tell her and touch her arm lightly to reassure her.

'Me nar know why yu stick wid de ole goat, but fi de pickney dem sake – me understand,' Miz Ruby would tell her.

Miz Ruby was a kind soul. She'd got Mummy the job in the cake factory. Four hours a day, five evenings a week. At first my father loved the idea of Mummy working. He thought he would give her less money for housekeeping. He tried that the first week, and I remember when Mummy put the food in front of him on Sunday and he nearly had a heart attack.

'What dis, eh?' he said in a shocked voice. 'How yu expect me fi eat dis! Dis couldn't feed a mouse.' He pushed the plate away and looked at my mother. 'But Alton, yu never give me enough money dis week, what yu expect,' she replied innocently. 'But Patsy yu a work,' he said. And my mother would go into a lengthy explanation of what she had done with her wages.

The following day, he would reluctantly give her the rest of the housekeeping money. My mother told my father that she was getting £8 wages but in fact she was really getting £12. I wanted to remark one day about this when my mother said, 'Chile, why yu mout so big? Shh!' putting her finger on her lips. 'It's our secret, baby,' she whispered, putting her arms around me. I felt good to know that I had been included in a big person's secret. The money paid for Mummy's return ticket to Jamaica as well as a little change for spending. It took eighteen months of secretly storing the money and goods Mummy was taking to JA.

Miz Ruby was the instigator and officer in charge of Plans A, B and C. All us children were excited to be part of the operation, and keeping it from my father was such a joke at the time, although afterwards when we got beaten, none of us were laughing. And the more Miz Ruby came to the house the more my father resented her. 'Dat woman is slack an outta order,' he would say after she had left. What he meant, I'm sure, was that she had sussed him out and took no notice of him. She encouraged Mummy all the more. It was Miz Ruby who came up with the idea to put the clock back. She said she had seen it done in the cinema. 'Yu know de woman leave de man sleeping inna bed, an take time ease herself out de house, an when him wake up inna morning an she gone, him tink seh it early an go back fi sleep. Dis time de woman gone bout her business.' She fell about laughing. We all started laughing at what we didn't know, but we were always glad for a good laugh, especially if it was at Daddy's expense.

'Now Patsy, put all yu grip dem in my house, and me will come to de airport with yu an help yu and ting.' She nodded her head. 'Nar worry about a ting, if yu husband Alton find out and him come fi me house, me will lick him in dat bald patch him trying fi cover up,

113

*Elliots ♡ → Selfish ♡*
*Similar to 'Full Stop'*
*- Grandma made common*
*mum.*

till him fart,' she said menacingly.

'All right,' said Daddy grabbing hold of Blossom who was the first in line for beating, which I thought was fair considering she was the oldest and got everything first. Pow! boft! thump! slap! Daddy was laying into her wickedly. Welts started to appear on her legs, from the leather strap which was well worn from previous beatings we had all received at some time or other. The way Daddy was going on you would have thought he was getting paid for it. He never did nothing for nothing. I hoped that Daddy would tire himself out and that by the time he got to me, who was third on the agenda for beatings, it would not bite so much. 'Did yu do it, Marcia?' he barked next. 'Who was it den?' he shouted. 'I don't know Daddy,' she bawled.

Whup! whup! whup! 'Yu liar yu,' he accused her. Here we go! My turn. 'Me knows yu is a little liar when yu ready, so me is not even gwan fi ask yu,' he said to me.

'It wasn't me,' I bawled, 'but I know who it is' – silence – 'it, it was Mummy,' I said as matter of factly as I could. Thump! slap! 'Yu too smart fi yu own good,' said Daddy.

When he got to Cassius, who was already bawling and wailing and screaming Daddy said, 'Chile, what do yu? Me no touch yu yet an yu a bawl,' and he pounced on him. They were both doing a kind of Arawak dance, Cassius to escape licks and Daddy making sure that he didn't.

Then we were all crying and howling, our skins stinging from the licks, Daddy shouting and barking at us. At the time, we weren't to know that it was purely his anger at my mother foiling him in her escape (thinking her too stupid usually to mastermind such a thing). He was deeply hurt. *– wife tricked him yet has also old be eg a hurt.*
*– not quite a redeeming quality ↗*

Well, life has to go on, and on it did go. I felt at the time that I wouldn't have minded being adopted for the six weeks, even if it meant a white family. At least I would be able to have bangers and mash, and fish and chips. Blossom's cooking left a dent in my stomach. It was awful and the more Daddy beat her the worse it got.

Sundays were a nightmare. From Saturday we all had to participate in the weekend cleaning: pick up the carpets and take them out the backyard and beat them; mop down the house from top to bottom. When it was dry, polish it. Wash the clothes, by hand. Everywhere had to be spick and span. Daddy would walk all over the house inspecting it and if he wasn't satisfied whoever was responsible was licked. I recall Cassius bearing the brunt of most of his dissatisfaction. Daddy had something about him, concerning Cassius, I don't know what, but Cassius was always singled out for punishment. There was no playing out with the other children. When the cleaning was finished, we had to prepare the dinner for Sunday: season up the chicken, and boil out the peas, and get our clothes ready for Sunday school. When all that was done, we had lessons. My father had trained as a school teacher in Jamaica, but because the qualifications were different over here in England, he could not practise publicly, so he practised on us.

'Wot yu mean yu don't know de answer? If yu cut a orange inna six an tek away two pieces how much leave?'

'Hmm, three pieces leave,' said Cassius.

'Bwoy, yu fool fi trut,' said Daddy, followed by two heavy arm movements across Cassius' head. 'Go work it out! Me nar know wat me do to deserve pickney like yus.' I privately thought what had we done to have a father like you, but was never brave enough to say it.

One night, I was awakened by noises out on the stairs, so I took time and crept out and there was my father. I am sure he was talking to someone but I couldn't see properly, and it would have meant me going out further to see, and I certainly wasn't risking that! But I remember the next morning my father was a different man. He gave us sixpence pocket money which was way over the top for him. Whatever had put him in this mood, I hoped it would happen again.

When the postcard came, we were all excited by it, 'Look, Mummy sent us a postcard! Jamaica look nice eh,' said Blossom. Daddy came up and snatched it out of her hand. After he'd read it, he ordered us back to our rooms. Mummy had not made any special reference to him in the postcard, which put him in a bad mood for the rest of the week.

It seemed ages since Mummy had gone. I was frightened that she would not come back for us, or send for us to go to her.

One Wednesday evening as we came home from school, the house seemed different. Mummy was home. Well, pure noise was filling the house. Mummy looked different. She had gotten fatter. Her skin colour had darkened and her eyes held a look that I had not seen before. She had inner peace.

'Look at me pickney dem,' she said. She had brought back fruits and fish and clothes and baskets and hats. It seemed as though she had brought back the whole of Jamaica with her, and just for us. It was like a party. Miz Ruby came round and she was laughing and joking and asking Mummy questions about home, and when Mummy gave her a bottle of white rum, she developed a permanent grin on her face. 'Oh Patsy yu shouldn't! Yu spoil me, but tank yu all de same,' said Miz Ruby.

When Daddy came home that evening, Lord a' mercy, it was like fire breaking out. 'Who tell yu seh yu can go a Jamaica,' shouted Daddy to Mummy. 'Yu tink seh yu's a big woman.' That sounded strange to us kids. Mummy was a big person and she could do what she liked. My mother as usual never answered him. 'Yu wait til later, yu gwan have fi pay for wot yu did fi me, gwan off like dat, no questions asked or nothin,' he said.

The police came. There was blood and glass broken all over the place. Cassius started to cry. My daddy was nowhere to be seen. My mother was very brave. She wasn't crying or anything. I couldn't understand the blood. She wasn't cut or anything. What did it mean? We'd all heard the noise and the shouting, even the glass breaking, but we hadn't dared go outside and investigate. But when we heard men talking we couldn't resist it. 'Blossom should go first, she's the oldest,' said Marcia, who was usually the most quiet one of the whole bunch of us. 'No, I'm not going,' said Blossom, cowardly. 'I'll go then,' I said bravely. I peeped around the door slowly. That's when I saw the police. 'Now, Mrs Hinds, if he troubles you again when you hit him with a brick, aim properly and knock him unconscious, luv,' said the officer. 'Yes, sir,' said Mummy.

When they had gone, Mummy briefly told us all the happenings. Daddy had made a beeline for her and she couldn't take it any more so she started throwing glasses at him and he persisted and then she picked up the brick which we used as a door stop and hit him. When Daddy came home he was like a bear. His head was in bandage. He spoke to no one.

I felt a personal triumph for Mummy – it would be a while yet before he'd raise his hand to her again.

117

- freak in story
- setting in India.

# ● Focus on theme

·······························

- Splits & conflicting personalities.

2 diff personalities

# Circus Cat Alley Cat

- wild animalistic cha.?
- misleads → about 2 cha?
  but real story - 1 cha.
- emphasis on T. of imagina~

## by Anita Desai

- Vivid imagery of imagina~

- how writer transforms e nurse in white uniform
  to death-defying circus performer is humorous.

1st perso~ → manipulated by child's imagina~.
negative → quite bias, exciting, vibrant.
innocent victim

- apprehen~ towards Anna
  (evokes curiosity as why she isn't a proper
  nanny.
- mostly 'bart inner thought of children.

I first saw Anna, the new 'nanny' of the English children who lived next door, in a pink stucco house, late one evening when she came to <u>hound</u> us out of the shrubbery where we were playing hide-and-seek, a game which, as anyone knows, grows exciting only at dinnertime. I crept behind a screen of bamboos and peered out at her through the polished bars of the bamboo stalks. She was large and heavily built, with very black bright eyes and a lot of wiry black hair. She bent down to pick up a neem switch and slapped it against her thigh as she called to us in a loud, sharp voice. And through the cage of bamboos, in that blue twilight, I saw the lawn turn to a sawdust covered stage floor and Nanny's white uniform into spangled pink tights and the switch in her hand to a long, whistling whip that cracked in the air which was filled no longer with the talking of mynah birds and the barks of pet dogs, but with the roars of tigers and the gibbering of apes. Sick with terror, I found I could scarcely breathe and preferred to creep over the manure pit to my own home than on to the lawn and face to face with Nanny.

My imagination was fired, no doubt, as much by the

- out of proper~ images

*(margin: vivid imagina~)*

*(margin: transforms~ overwhelm by Anna.)*

118

fact that I had only that morning heard that Nanny came from a circus where she had worked as cat-trainer, as by the cracking of the switch in her hand and her hefty shoulders and authoritative voice. How the staid, plain, and entirely unimaginative family of Bates could choose a circus performer to be a Nanny for their children is an eternal mystery, though they endeavoured to explain it to us as an act of charity. Anna, they told us (her real name, or stage name, was Shakti – Strength! Power! – but the Bateses preferred to call her by the more tame and domestic name of Anna) was a Malabar girl who had been born into the circus, and had trained the big cats since she was thirteen. Her special 'breath-taking, death-defying, terror-striking' act was to drape a tiger over her shoulders and stand on the backs of two lions whom she would then order to emit great, rumbling roars that made her large frame tremble all over and the tiger snarl. Dressed in parrot-green tights and a lilac shirt with silver spangles, her fierce mane of hair standing on end, she must have looked a sight. Then she married the boy who fed the cats. The boy was ambitious. In no time, he had taught her that a woman's place is her home and was straddling the lions himself and wrapping the tiger round his own neck. Anna, in a spurt of cat-like temper, left. By that time she had a baby, and when Mrs Bates found her, she and the child were near starvation, begging on a Daryaganj Street. Mrs Bates gave her a white uniform and put bath-salts in her tub in order to wash off that special circus odour of elephant manure and cat sweat; she was installed as the children's Nanny, and her baby put in a cradle on the back verandah and fed on milk and oranges.

All this played real havoc on our imagination, as

119

nothing had ever done before. She had only to rattle the knobs of the windows and doors as she banged them shut against the summer heat, to make us feel we were being shut into our cages. We would no longer walk, or run, but prowl. We would not hop or skip, but spring and leap. Even our voices changed. Anna had only to come into the room with a tricycle or our skipping-ropes, and we would feel the trainer had arrived, wooden chair in hand, to practise the act, and in this spirit we would play the games she ordered us to play. Anna had only to sit down at the breakfast table and cut the bread into slices for us, to make us think of it as a great hunk of fresh meat, dripping with scarlet blood, and we would shudder as we gnawed at it. A cooking-spoon in Anna's hand would become a biting, snapping, snaky whip. A plain brooch pinned in her lapel would change the plain white uniform to a gaudy, satin stage costume. When the lights were switched on at night, the brightness of Anna's eyes was the brightness of a stage-performer's eyes in the glare of white-hot arc lamps. No matter how hard Mrs Bates tried to domesticate her and turn her into a tame alley-cat, a nice, motherly pussy-cat, Anna remained to us the 'breath-taking, death-defying, terror-striking' Anna of the circus. Poor Anna herself played no part in this. No matter how hard we tried, and how cleverly, she never spoke of the circus once. Yet the very house, with its Rangoon creeper, its worn rugs and nursery pictures, became the Big Top for us, the dinner-bell, the big drums, the lights, the spotlights of the stage. We lived in a constant quiver of thrill upon thrill. I dreamt of cats all the night, long-striped cats leaping in the air, great cats shaking their manes as they roared, their muscles rippling under the smooth skin, the shining hair. They sprang soundlessly from dream to dream, landing softly on my eyelids, and from strangers of the jungle they became companions of the long nights of excitement.

And then Anna's baby vanished. I came across Anna in the garden one day, her hair more disordered than ever, her eyes red from weeping. 'My baby's gone!' she cried theatrically, 'My baby's been taken away. Oh God, oh God, give my baby back to me – but I'll never see her again – she's been taken away from me.' And I joined wholeheartedly in the weeping to think that God had taken the child at such a tender age and left poor Anna all alone. As I ran back to the house to tell my mother, I wondered if the baby had suddenly been taken ill, because she had seemed very healthy and well only the previous day. My mother was, for this reason, equally shocked and immediately went to see Anna.

Anna wept on her shoulders, looking quite thin and pathetic in her sorrow. My mother pressed her hand and soothed her, 'What God decrees, we must accept Anna. It is sad but it must be, Anna.' On her way out, she looked in on Mrs Bates, and asked, 'When is the funeral to be?'

'The funeral?' Mrs Bates jumped. 'What funeral?'

'Why, of poor Anna's baby!'

'Anna's baby? Why, is it dead?'

We were nonplussed that the mistress of the house should not have heard of the tragedy yet. My mother and I interrupted each other in trying to tell her what had happened and were horrified when the kind old missionary's wife chortled and clapped her hand over her mouth to stop her laughter.

'The baby dead!' she cried. 'Whatever gave you the idea? It's only that Anna's husband and his family came and took it away. We're trying to get it back, only the circus has moved to Bombay now so it will be a bit difficult. We're sending Anna off to try though.'

That was the last we saw of Anna for a long time. The next time was several years later when we went to see a circus and found Shakti's name on the handbill, and a picture of Anna with a snarling tiger on her shoulders. She was smiling hugely.

We could scarcely wait till she appeared and then were so excited we could not even applaud. We watched out for her baby and wondered if it had grown into the little girl who was somersaulting in the sawdust and tumbling around with a deeply preoccupied expression on her thin face. But throughout the performance, the thought uppermost in my mind was: where is Anna's husband? And I had a vivid picture of Anna in a great cage, gnawing, gnawing upon a great, bleeding hunk of flesh, Anna snarling at the people who came to snatch it from her, Anna throwing back her mane and giving a great roar of triumph, Anna the queen of the circus cats, Anna the circus cat . . .

# More than just the Disease

**by Bernard MacLaverty**

As he unpacked his case Neil kept hearing his mother's voice. *Be tidy at all times, then no one can surprise you.* This was a strange house he'd come to, set in the middle of a steep terraced garden. Everything in it seemed of an unusual design; the wardrobe in which he hung his good jacket was of black lacquer with a yellow inlay of exotic birds. *A little too ornate for my taste – vulgar almost.* And pictures – there were pictures hanging everywhere, portraits, landscapes, sketches. *Dust gatherers.* The last things in his case were some comics and he laid them with his ironed and folded pyjamas on the pillow of the bottom bunk and went to join the others.

They were all sitting in the growing dark of the large front room, Michael drinking hot chocolate, Anne his sister with her legs flopped over the arm of the chair, Dr Middleton squeaking slowly back and forth in the rocking-chair while his wife moved around preparing to go out.

'Now, boys, you must be in bed by ten thirty at the latest. Anne can sit up until we come back if she wants. We'll not be far away and if anything does happen you can phone "The Seaview".' She spent some time looking in an ornamental jug for a pen to write down the number. 'I can find nothing in this house yet.'

'We don't need Anne to babysit,' said Michael. 'We're perfectly capable of looking after ourselves. Isn't that right Neil?' Neil nodded. He didn't like

123

Michael involving him in an argument with the rest of the family. He had to have the tact of a guest; sit on the fence yet remain Michael's friend.

'Can we not stay up as late as Anne?' asked Michael.

'Anne is fifteen years of age. Please, Michael, it's been a long day. Off to bed.'

'But Mama, Neil and I . . .'

'Michael.' The voice came from the darkness of the rocking-chair and had enough threat in it to stop Michael. The two boys got up and went to their bedroom.

Neil lifted his pyjamas and went to the bathroom. He dressed for bed buttoning the jacket right up to his neck and went back with his clothes draped over his arm. Michael was half-dressed.

'That was quick,' he said. He bent his thin arms, flexing his biceps. 'I only wear pyjama bottoms. Steve McQueen, he-man,' and he thumped his chest before climbing to the top bunk. They lay and talked and talked – about their first year at the school, how lucky they had been to have been put in the same form, who they hated most. The Crow with his black gown and beaky nose, the Moon with his pallid round face, wee Hamish with his almost mad preoccupation with ruling red lines. Once Neil had awkwardly ruled a line which showed the two bumps of his fingers protruding beyond the ruler and wee Hamish had pounced on it.

'What are these bumps? Is this a drawing of a camel, boy?' Everybody except Neil had laughed and if there was one thing he couldn't abide it was to be laughed at. A voice whispered that it was a drawing of his girlfriend's chest.

Neil talked about the Scholarship examination and the day he got his results. When he saw the fat envelope on the mat he knew his life would change – if you got

124

the thin envelope you had failed, a fat one with coloured forms meant that you had passed. What Neil did not say was that his mother had cried, kneeling in the hallway hugging and kissing him. He had never seen anyone cry with happiness before and it worried him a bit. Nor did he repeat what she had said with her eyes shining. *Now you'll be at school with the sons of doctors and lawyers.*

Anne opened the door and hissed into the dark. 'You've got to stop talking right now. Get to sleep.' She was in a cotton nightdress which became almost transparent with the light of the hallway behind her. Neil saw her curved shape outlined to its margins. He wanted her to stay there but she slammed the door.

After that they whispered and had a farting competition. They heard Michael's father and mother come in, make tea and go to bed. It was ages before either of them slept. All the time Neil was in agonies with his itch but he did not want to scratch in case Michael should feel the shaking communicated to the top bunk.

In the morning Neil was first awake and tiptoed to the bathroom with all his clothes to get dressed. He took off his pyjama jacket and looked at himself in the mirror. Every morning he hoped that it would have miraculously disappeared overnight but it was still there crawling all over his chest and shoulders: his psoriasis – a redness with an edge as irregular as a map and the skin flaking and scumming off the top. Its pattern changed from week to week but only once had it appeared above his collar line. That week his mother had kept him off school. He turned his back on the mirror and put on a shirt, buttoning it up to the neck. He wondered if he should wear a tie to breakfast but his mother's voice had nothing to say on the subject. Breakfast wasn't a meal like in his own house when

125

he and his mother sat down at table and had cereal and tea and toast with sometimes a boiled egg. Here people just arrived and poured themselves cornflakes and went off to various parts of the room, or even the house, to eat them. The only still figure was the doctor himself. He sat at the corner of the table reading the *Scotsman* and drinking coffee. He wore blue running shoes and no socks and had a T-shirt on. Except for his receding M-shaped hairline he did not look at all like a doctor. In Edinburgh anytime Neil had seen him he wore a dark suit and a spotted bow-tie.

Anne came in. '*Guten Morgen, mein Papa.* Hello Neil.' She was bright and washed with her yellow hair in a knot on the top of her head. Neil thought she was the most beautiful girl he had ever seen up close. She wore a pair of denims cut down to shorts so that there were frayed fringes about her thighs. She also had what his mother called *a figure*. She ate her cornflakes noisily and the doctor did not even raise his eyes from the paper. *Close your mouth when you're eating, please. Others have to live with you.*

'Some performance last night, eh Neil?' she said.

'Pardon?'

'Daddy, they talked till all hours.'

Her father turned a page of the paper and his hand groped out like a blind man's to find his coffee.

'Sorry,' said Neil.

'I'm only joking,' said Anne and smiled at him. He blushed because she looked directly into his eyes and smiled at him as if she liked him. He stumbled to his feet.

'Thank you for the breakfast,' he said to the room in general and went outside to the garden where Michael was sitting on the steps.

'Where did you get to? You didn't even excuse

yourself from the table,' said Neil.

'I wasn't at the table, small Fry,' said Michael. He was throwing pea-sized stones into an ornamental pond at a lower level.

'One minute you were there and the next you were gone.'

'I thought it was going to get heavy.'

'What?'

'I know the signs. The way the old man reads the paper. Coming in late last night.'

'Oh.'

Neil lifted a handful of multi-coloured gravel and fed the pieces singly into his other hand and lobbed them at the pool. They made a nice plip noise.

'Watch it,' said Michael. He stilled Neil's throwing arm with his hand. 'Here comes Mrs Wan.'

'Who's she?'

An old woman in a bottle-green cardigan and baggy mouse-coloured trousers came stepping one step at a time down towards them. She wore a puce-coloured hat like a turban and, although it was high summer, a pair of men's leather gloves.

'Good morning, boys,' she said. Her voice was the most superior thing Neil had ever heard, even more so than his elocution teacher's. 'And how are you this year, Benjamin?'

'Fine. This is my friend Neil Fry.' Neil stood up and nodded. She was holding secateurs and a flat wooden basket. He knew that she would find it awkward to shake hands so he did not offer his.

'How do you do? What do you think of my garden, young man?'

'It's very good. Tidy.'

'Let's hope it remains that way throughout your stay,' she said and continued her sideways stepping down until she reached the compost heap at the bottom beyond the ornamental pool.

'Who is she?' asked Neil.

'She owns the house. Lets it to us for the whole of the summer.'

'But where does she live when you're here?'

'Up the back in a caravan. She's got ninety million cats.' Mrs Wan's puce turban threaded in and out of the flowers as she weeded and pruned. It was a dull overcast day and the wind was moving the brightly coloured rose blooms.

'Fancy a swim?' asked Michael.

'Too cold. Anyway I told you I can't swim.'

'You don't have to swim. Just horse around. It's great.'

'Naw.'

Michael threw his whole handful of gravel chirping into the pond and went up the steps to the house.

That afternoon the shelf of cloud moved inland and the sky over the Atlantic became blue. The wind dropped and Dr Middleton observed that the mare's-tails were a good sign. The whole family went down the hundred yards to the beach, each one carrying something – a basket, a deckchair, a lilo.

'Where else in the world but Scotland would we have the beach to ourselves on a day like this?' said Mrs Middleton. The doctor agreed with a grunt. Michael got stripped to his swimming trunks and they taught Neil to play boule in the hard sand near the water. The balls were of bright grooved steel and he enjoyed trying to lob them different ways until he finally copied the doctor who showed him how to put back-spin on them. Anne wore a turquoise bikini and kept hooking her fingers beneath the elastic of her pants and snapping them out to cover more of her bottom. She did this every time she bent to pick up her boule and Neil came to watch for it. When they stopped playing Michael and his sister ran off to leap about in the breakers – large curling walls, glass-green, which nearly knocked them off their feet. From where he stood Neil could only hear their cries faintly. He went and sat down with the doctor and his wife.

'Do you not like the water?' she asked. She was lying on a sunbed, gleaming with suntan oil. She had her dress rucked up beyond her knees and her shoulder straps loosened.

'No. It's too cold.'

'The only place *I'll* ever swim again is the Med,' said the doctor.

'Sissy,' said his wife, without opening her eyes. Neil lay down and tried to think of a better reason for not swimming. His mother had one friend who occasionally phoned for her to go to the Commonwealth Pool. When she really didn't feel like it there was only one excuse that seemed to work.

At tea Michael took a perverse pleasure out of telling him again and again how warm the water was and Anne innocently agreed with him.

The next day was scorching hot. Even at breakfast time they could see the heat corrugating the air above the slabbed part of the garden.

'You *must* come in for a swim today, Fry. I'm boiled already,' said Michael.

'The forecast is twenty-one degrees,' said the doctor from behind his paper. Anne whistled in appreciation.

Neil's thighs were sticking to the plastic of his chair. He said, 'My mother forgot to pack my swimming trunks. I looked yesterday.'

Mrs Middleton, in a flowing orange dressing-gown,

spoke over her shoulder from the sink. 'Borrow a pair of Michael's.' Before he could stop her she had gone off with wet hands in search of extra swimming trunks.

'Couldn't be simpler,' she said, setting a navy blue pair with white side panels on the table in front of Neil.

'I'll get mine,' said Michael and dashed to his room. Anne sat opposite Neil on the Formica kitchen bench-top swinging her legs. She coaxed him to come swimming, again looking into his eyes. He looked down and away from them.

'Come on, Neil. Michael's not much fun in the water.'

'The fact is,' said Neil, 'I've got my period.'

There was a long silence and a slight rustle of the *Scotsman* as Dr Middleton looked over the top of it. Then Anne half-slid, half-vaulted off the bench and ran out. Neil heard her make funny snorts in her nose.

'That's too bad,' said the doctor and got up and went out of the room shutting the door behind him. Neil heard Anne's voice and her father's, then he heard the bedroom door shut. He folded his swimming trunks and set them on the sideboard. Mrs Middleton gave a series of little coughs and smiled at him.

'Can I help you with the dishes?' he asked. There was something not right.

'Are you sure you're well enough?' she said smiling. Neil nodded and began to lift the cups from various places in the room. She washed and he dried with a slow thoroughness.

'Neil, nobody is going to force you to swim. So you can feel quite safe.'

Michael came in with his swimming gear in a roll under his arm.

'Ready, small Fry?'

'Michael, could I have a word? Neil, could you leave

those bathing trunks back in Michael's wardrobe?'

On the beach the boys lay down on the sand. Michael hadn't spoken since they left the house. He walked in front, he picked the spot, he lay down and Neil followed him. The sun was hot and again they had the beach to themselves. Neil picked up a handful of sand and examined it as he spilled it out slowly.

'I bet you there's at least one speck of gold on this beach,' he said.

'That's a bloody stupid thing to say.'

'I'll bet you there is.'

Michael rolled over turning his back. 'I can pick them.'

'What?'

'I can really pick them.'

'What do you mean?'

'I might as well have asked a girl to come away on holiday.'

Neil's fist bunched in the sand.

'What's the use of somebody who won't go in for a dip?'

'I can't, that's all.'

'My Mum says you must have a very special reason. What is it, Fry?'

Neil opened his hand and some of the damp, deeper sand remained in little segments where he had clenched it. He was almost sure Anne had laughed.

'I'm not telling you.'

'Useless bloody Mama's boy,' said Michael. He got up flinging a handful of sand at Neil and ran down to the water. Some of the sand went into Neil's eyes, making him cry. He knuckled them clear and blinked, watching Michael jump, his elbows up, as each glass wave rolled at him belly-high.

Neil shouted hopelessly towards the sea. 'That's the last time I'm getting you into the pictures.'

He walked back towards the house. He had been here a night, a day and a morning. It would be a whole week before he could get home. Right now he felt he *was* a Mama's boy. He just wanted to climb the stair and be with her behind the closed door of their house. This had been the first time in his life he had been away from her and, although he had been reluctant because of this very thing, she had insisted that he could not turn down an invitation from the doctor's family. *It will teach you how to conduct yourself in good society.*

At lunch time Michael did not speak to him but made up salad rolls and took them on to the patio. Anne and her father had gone into the village on bicycles. Neil sat at the table chewing his roll with difficulty and staring in front of him. *If there is one thing I cannot abide it's a milk bottle on the table.* Mrs Middleton was the only one left for him to talk to.

'We met Mrs Wan this morning,' he said.

'Oh did you? She's a rum bird – feeding all those cats.'

'How many has she?'

'I don't know. They're never all together at the same time. She's a Duchess, you know?'

'A real one?'

'Yes. I can't remember her title – from somewhere in England. She married some Oriental and lived in the Far East. Africa too for a time. When he died she came home. Look.' She waved her hand at all the bric-à-brac. 'Look at this.' She went to a glass-fronted cabinet and took out what looked like a lace ball. It was made of ivory and inside was another ball with just as intricately carved mandarins and elephants and palm leaves, with another one inside that again.

*Neil—Small Social circle*

'The question is how did they carve the one inside. It's all one piece.'

Neil turned it over in his hands marvelling at the mystery. He handed it carefully back.

'You wouldn't want to play boule with that,' he said.

'Isn't it exquisitely delicate?'

*- be very polite, observe social grace.*

He nodded and said, 'Thank you for the lunch. It was very n<u>ourish</u>ing.' *- lack social grace, instead of thanking her gauche awkward.*

*of attitude they make a more social cont.*
He wandered outside in the garden and sat for a while by the pool. It was hot and the air was full of the noise of insects and bees moving in and out the flowers. He went down to the beach and saw that his friend Michael had joined up with some other boys to play cricket. He sat down out of sight of them at the side of a sand-dune. He lay back and closed his eyes. They had laughed at him in school when he said he didn't know what l.b.w. meant. He had been given a free cricket bat but there was hardly a mark on it because he couldn't seem to hit the ball. It was so hard and came at him so fast that he was more interested in getting out of its way than playing any fancy strokes. Scholarship boys were officially known as foundationers but the boys called them '<u>fundies</u>' or 'fundaments'. When he asked what it meant somebody told him to look it up in a dictionary. 'Part of body on which one sits; buttocks; anus.'

*pen, vulnerable, so due to background* *end to being a ship boy.* *g ff. his family hard.* *stk as usher ema*

He lifted his head and listened. At first he thought it was the noise of a distant seagull but it came again and he knew it wasn't. He looked up to the top of the sand-dune and saw a kitten, its tiny black tail upright and quivering.

'Pshhh-wshhh.'

He climbed the sand and lifted it. It miaowed thinly. He stroked its head and back and felt the frail fish bones of its ribs. It purred and he carried it back to the house. He climbed the steps behind the kitchen and

*k & father figure*

saw a caravan screened by a thick hedge. The door was open and he had to hold it steady with his knee before he could knock on it.

'Come in,' Mrs Wan's voice called. Neil stepped up into the van. After the bright sunlight it was gloomy inside. It smelt of old and cat. He saw Mrs Wan sitting along one wall with her feet up.

'I found this and thought maybe it was yours,' said Neil handing the cat over to her. She scolded it.

'You little monkey,' she said and smiled at Neil. 'This cat is a black sheep. He's always wandering off. Thank you, young man. It was very kind of you to take the trouble to return him.'

'It was no trouble.'

She was dressed as she had been the day before except for the gloves. Her hands were old and her fingers bristled with rings. She waved at him as he turned to go.

'Just a minute. Would you like something to drink – as a reward?' She stood up and rattled in a cupboard above the sink.

'I think some tonic water is all I can offer you. Will that do?' She didn't give him a clean glass but just rinsed one for a moment under the thin trickle from the swan-neck tap at the tiny sink. She chased three cats away from the covered bench seat and waved him to sit down. Because the glass was not very clean the bubbles adhered to its sides. He saw that nothing was clean as he looked about the place. There were several tins of Kit-e-Kat opened on the draining-board and a silver fork encrusted with the stuff lay beside them. There were saucers all over the floor with milk which had evaporated in the heat leaving yellow rings. Everything was untidy. He set his glass between a pile of magazines and a marmalade pot on the table. She asked him his name and about his school and where he lived and about his father. Neil knew that his mother would call her nosey but he thought that she seemed interested in all his answers. She listened intently, blinking and staring at him with her face slightly turned as if she had a deaf ear.

'My father died a long time ago,' he said.

'And your mother?'

'She's alive.'

'And what does she do for a living?'

'She works in the cinema.'

'Oh how interesting. Is she an actress?'

'No. She just works there. With a torch. She gets me in free – for films that are suitable for me. Sometimes I take my friend Michael with me.'

'Is that the boy below?'

'Yes.'

'I thought his name was Benjamin. But how marvellous that you can see all these films free.' She clapped her ringed hands together and seemed genuinely excited. 'I used to love the cinema. The cartoons were my favourite. And the newsreels. I'll bet you're very popular when a good picture comes to town.'

'Yes I am,' said Neil and smiled and sipped his tonic.

'Let's go outside and talk. It's a shame to waste such a day in here.' Neil offered his arm as she lowered herself from the step to the ground.

'What a polite young man.'

'That's my mother's fault.'

They sat on the deckchairs facing the sun and she lit a cigarette, holding it between her jewelled fingers. Her face was brown and criss-crossed with wrinkles.

'Why aren't you in swimming on such a day?' she asked.

Neil hesitated, then heard himself say, 'I can't. I've got a disease.'

'What is it?'

Again he paused but this old woman seemed to demand the truth.

'A thing – on my chest.'

'Let me see?' she said and leaned forward. He was amazed to find himself unbuttoning his shirt and showing her his mark. In the sunlight it didn't look so red. She scrutinized it and hummed, pursing her mouth and biting her lower lip.

'Why does it stop you bathing?'

Neil shrugged and began to button up when she stopped him.

'Let the sun at it. I'm sure it can do no harm.' He left his shirt lying open. 'When I was in Africa I worked with lepers.'

'Lepers?'

'Yes. So the sight of you doesn't worry me,' she said. 'Watch that you don't suffer from more than just the disease.'

'I don't understand.'

'It's bad enough having it without being shy about it as well.'

'Have you got leprosy now?'

'No. It's not as contagious as everybody says.'

Neil finished his tonic and lay back in the chair. The sun was bright and hot on his chest. He listened to Mrs Wan talking about leprosy, of how the lepers lost their fingers and toes, not because of the disease but because they had lost all feeling in them and they broke and damaged them without knowing. Eventually they got gangrene. Almost all the horrible things of leprosy, she said, were secondary. Suddenly he heard Michael's voice.

'Mrs Wan, Mum says could you tell her where . . .' his voice tailed off seeing Neil's chest, '. . . the cheese grater is?'

'Do you know, I think I brought it up here.' She got up and stepped slowly into the caravan. Neil closed over his shirt and began to button it. Neither boy said a word.

At tea Michael spoke to him as if they were friends again and in bed that night it was Neil's suggestion that they go for a swim.

'Now? Are you mad?'

'They say it's warmer at night.'

'Yeah and we could make dummies in the beds like Clint Eastwood.'

'They don't *have* to look like Clint Eastwood.' They both laughed quiet sneezing laughs.

After one o'clock they dropped out of the window and ran to the beach. For almost half an hour in the pale darkness Neil thrashed and shivered. Eventually he sat down to wait in the warmer shallows, feeling the withdrawing sea hollow the sand around him. Further out, Michael whooped and rode the breakers like a shadow against their whiteness.

137

# Activities

## FOCUS ON PLOT

### An Astrologer's Day

**1** Reread the opening paragraph that sets the tone for the story. Describe four factors that help to create an atmosphere of magic and mysticism. Explain why this becomes important later in the story.

**2** Make a list of clues given earlier in the story which hint at what is revealed at the end.

**3** The narrator states '. . . he knew no more of what was going to happen to others than he knew what was going to happen to himself next minute . . . Yet he said things which pleased and astonished everyone.' Based on the information given in the story, write a beginner's guide entitled How To Tell Fortunes. Swap guides and tell a partner his or her fortune.

### The Pieces of Silver

**1** Draw up a set of rules that the teachers could have made for children at this school. This might have been a school in the 1940s. Find an adult to interview who was at school forty to fifty years ago.

**2** Write a character profile of the acting Head, Mr Chase, under the following headings:

- physical appearance
- personality
- relationship with staff
- relationship with pupils

How does his character contribute to the plot?

**3** There is a double twist in the plot, and the children get double satisfaction. Explain how this double twist works.

## Comparative task

Both stories in this section have been very carefully planned in terms of:

- the point of view from which the story is told
- the situation, or how the author chooses to set up the story
- the initial fiction 'trigger' or incident which makes the story take an interesting turn
- resolution, or how the author chooses to end or leave the story.

Identify these elements in each story. Plan a story of your own using this framework. If you go on to write the story, you can also encourage your readers to follow certain leads and then surprise them.

## FOCUS ON CHARACTER

## Crime and Punishment

**1** The boy in the story is described as an angel and a gorilla.

Draw a simple grid with two columns, one headed 'angel', the other 'gorilla'. Find three pieces of evidence to support each. Which do you think he is? What would R. K. Narayan want us to think?

**2** This story is unusual in that the four main characters are just referred to as 'the boy', 'the teacher' and 'the parents'. What effect do you think this has? Give the characters some names and use them when reading the first page again. Has your attitude to the characters changed in any way? Try again with a different set of names.

**3** In order to get his own way the boy uses a number of different strategies. For example, he:

- cries
- makes a joke about soldiers fighting back
- threatens to tell his mother
- demands that the teacher play with him
- points to the red mark where the teacher hit him
- eventually runs off to find his parents.

How does the teacher respond? Choose three of the boy's strategies and rewrite the appropriate paragraphs so that the teacher responds in a way more likely to gain the upper hand.

## Warrior Woman and Easter Hat

**1** In both stories, set in Toronto, Nancy Chong describes events involving her mother. She also offers us insights into what it is like to be female, Chinese and living in Canada in the 1960s. Her perspective in each story is that of a young child. With a partner, role-play a dialogue between Nancy as a teenager and an inquisitive friend in which Nancy explains how she feels about the visit to the cinema and the purchase of the Easter hat.

**2** In *Warrior Woman*, Nancy's mother gossiped with Hong's wife. In playscript form write their conversation. Remember, you have the evidence from two stories. You will find some additional information about Nancy Chong and her family in the section about authors (see page 153).

## Comparative task

When writing a story about childhood, a writer has to decide whether to tell the story in the child's own words (as Nancy Chong did) or to write about the child from a storyteller's perspective (as R. K. Narayan did). Choose an incident (real or imagined) from your own childhood and describe it briefly, once in the first person, and once in the third person by an adult storyteller. What were the advantages and disadvantages of each method?

## FOCUS ON SETTING

### Kill to Eat

*To what extent is this true?*

**1** The setting of *Kill to Eat* a story (Stradbroke Island) is very important for the plot, yet the story contains no extended passages describing place. Gather as much evidence as you can about the island. Write an opening paragraph before 'My father worked for the Government', which describes Stradbroke. (Now turn to page 152 at the end of the Activities section for the author's own description of Stradbroke.)

**2** 'Father spoke for the first time since we had killed the kookaburra.' The punishment to follow was regarded by the children as worse than a beating, yet no one protested. Draft two alternative endings from this point onwards. Try to concentrate on producing an ending which suits the cultural environment in which the events take place.

**3** Write a story set in an area which you know very well. Try to make the plot resemble that of *Kill to Eat*, but you will need to change some aspects in order to make it appropriate to the setting (for example, the creature that is killed and the punishment will need to change).

## What Do You Do in Winter?

**1** In this story the town is personified, happier in the winter months than 'dressing up' in the summer for English strangers. To get a clearer answer to the question about how the town behaves in winter draw a map or plan which represents the significant places within the town. Label the places with names of the main characters and the events associated with them.

**2** It is easy to imagine this story turned into a play. Describe, in alphabetical order, the characters who appear in it, with a brief description of each one to help the actor interpret the character. Represent this as the cast list at the opening of a play.

**3** The author feels some injustice about the Eisteddfod winner, a sense shared by the audience: 'Silence met the judge's speech'. The actual winner is an outsider. How does this community feel about outsiders? Imagine you visit this small town twice, once in summer and once, to see the Eisteddfod, in winter. On each occasion send a postcard home giving some sense of an outsider's viewpoint.

## The Steel Windpipe

1. The setting is very important in this story. Try to imagine this story made into a film. Produce a one-page story-board which outlines the development of events. Try to think in terms of setting and viewpoint. Describe the setting inside and outside, long-shot and close-up, in the hospital and in the doctor's quarters. Concentrate particularly on the opening and closing shots.

2. The doctor's isolation forces him to be braver than he really wants to be. Find examples where his professional exterior is hiding a very nervous and insecure young man.

3. Hospital narratives regularly fill our television screens. How might an accident like *The Steel Windpipe* be handled in an episode of *Casualty*? How might the story change? Remember, some of the changes would be to do with history and geography, others to do with differences between stories in print and stories on television.

### Comparative task

Choose any three stories in this anthology, other than those in this section. Write a postcard home for each location. Try to match the mood of the description to that of the story and, where you can, hint at the events which take place.

## FOCUS ON CONTEXT

## The Gold Cadillac

**1** Mildred Taylor was born in Mississippi but her father decided to move North when she was three weeks old to avoid the segregation and overt racism of the South. Think carefully about why the father in the story decides to drive the Cadillac to Mississippi. However, he sells the car soon after the journey. Why do you think that is? Discuss the mixed feelings that he must have had, including his hopes for the future.

**2** 'We reached the Mississippi state line and soon after we heard a police siren.' Rewrite the narrative from the mother's point of view. Take it to the point where the narrator, 'lois, falls asleep with the knife in her hand. Remember the mother is more aware of the segregation in the South than the children. Your writing should reflect the mother's concerns.

## Poinsettias

**1** Under the following headings list what you know about the lives of: Marika's family; The van Reenens; Rebecca; Jan Venter. What does this information tell you about relationships between them?

**2** This story is set in South Africa during the time of apartheid which involved oppression and discrimination against the black majority by a government of white people. Can you find examples of such discrimination in the story? For many years the media was censored. Journalists who wanted to write about apartheid often had to work secretly. Assume you are a journalist investigating child labour and tell the story of what has happened on Jan Venter's farm.

**3** Reread the last paragraph. Look carefully at the detailed actions contained within it, for example: looking at the fallen poinsettia, grabbing the branch. Veronica's actions at the end are symbolic. In groups make a still image to represent the final scene.

## Robert and the Dog

**1** Throughout *Robert and the Dog* the contrast between Robert's home life and that of his employer is clearly illustrated. Map out the positive and negative aspects of Robert's life. Support your ideas with evidence from the story.

**2** 'Robert began to feel like a human being, and he felt extremely grateful to his new employers.' Yet his actions at the end of the story will mean his dismissal. Give a number of reasons for and against Robert's decision. Hot-seat Robert and the doctor to explore their different viewpoints.

**3** Ken Saro-Wiwa was a political activist in Nigeria who was a committed campaigner on human rights and environmental issues. He died for his beliefs in 1995. Yet in *Robert and the Dog* he chooses a simple story to question the way in which human life is valued. Discuss ways in which humans and animals are valued in Britain. As a charity commissioner, you have decided how to distribute £100,000 of lottery funds to Save the Children and the R.S.P.C.A. In a letter, explain to the two charities your decision.

# The Man

**1** At the end of colonial rule ordinary people who had struggled for independence had high hopes about achieving the equality and justice that they had previously been denied:

> the father-founder of the nation, the enlightened guide and saviour of the people, the great helmsman, the president-for-life, the commander-in-chief of the armed forces and the beloved father of the people lived in a vast palace out of bounds to the ordinary citizen.

As this passage suggests, these hopes have not always been met. What can you find out about the Congo where the author was born?

**2** From the start of the story there is a feeling of ruthlessness and oppression. What evidence can you find to support this view? List your answers.

**3** E. B. Dongala has been described as a major satirist. For example, he creates a security system for the palace which is larger than life. Can you find further examples of exaggeration and satirical writing in the story? In pairs write a television sketch which pokes fun at something you feel strongly about.

## Comparative task

Inequality, or injustice, is a key feature of each story in this section. All arise from real life situations. Write a speech entitled *Injustice*. Draw upon these stories as well as using other knowledge you may have. You may also wish to draw upon situations from your own experience. You will need to identify your audience.

## FOCUS ON LANGUAGE

## Why Apes Look Like People

**1** In a wide range of stories, from folk tales to Disney, we are used to animals which talk and have human characteristics. When animals are described as behaving like people this is known as anthropomorphism. Gather as many examples of anthropomorphism as you can up to the time when the animals consciously decide to become like people, for example:

| the capital D in 'the Deer' family | implies a human surname rather than a species |
| the Robins visit a sick relative | implies human social behaviour |

**2** This story is taken from a book of 'Black Folktales'. 'The Lord' and many of the animals speak in a dialect taken straight from the black people of the American South. For example, the Rabbit says, 'I've gotten used to that, Lord', and 'Water's fine, Lord . . . plenty tree-leaves . . . if you'd hush up.' This is not standard English, but it is a form of speech with a recognisable set of rules. Study this dialect carefully then continue the story using the same form of language in the dialogue – assume that the animals revisit the Lord in order to complain that there wasn't enough oil to go around.

# Full Stop

**1** From reading between the lines, what can you tell about Carmen and Richie, their mother and father, Normy, and, of course, Grandma? Read the letters carefully and try to piece together a description of each character. Where do your sympathies lie?

**2** Grandma's letter has no punctuation or paragraphs and has a distinctly chatty style. After the first reply, Carmen's is well-punctuated, and more clearly organised, though still informal. Examine closely the differing styles of the two writers. Continue the correspondence with two more letters from each. Try to develop events slowly over time and to maintain the letter-writing style of each character.

# The Escape

**1** 'I loved my father'. Given the way that the father treats his family you may be surprised by this statement. Yet the writer manages to describe even the most violent actions in an almost humorous way. Find examples of how she manages to tell the tale without turning it into a depressing story about child abuse.

**2** The adults in this story speak mainly Jamaican English:

- Work out some rules of this dialect that would help someone else speak it. For example, 'me' is used as the pronoun where you would expect 'I' in standard English.

- From the story choose three examples of Jamaican English and turn them into standard English. What effect does it have upon what is said and upon the story?

## Comparative task

> For a long time after the Lord created the world, the only creatures on it were the animals.

> My grandmother writes without commas or full stops

> 'Who put de clock back, eh!!'

Examine each opening sentence carefully. To what degree does each sentence give a clue as to the story which is to follow and the use of language within it?

## FOCUS ON THEME

## Circus Cat Alley Cat

**1** Anna is seen by the children as a frightening figure. Why? Read again the paragraph beginning: 'All this played real havoc on our imagination'. Make a list of everyday items and actions, and describe how the children viewed them, for example:

| closing doors and windows | *become* | shutting into cages |
| slices of bread | *become* | hunks of fresh meat dripping blood |

**2** The children obviously have a strong image of Anna. Include the material above in a poem describing Anna. Try to reflect the children's perceptions of her.

**3** Anna's real life is very different from the one the children create for her. She even loses her own Malabar name when she is 'rescued' by an English family. In the story

find evidence to show what her life was really like.
Interview her on a television chat show.

## More than just the Disease

**1** One theme of the story is to do with class. Neil's holiday
with the Middletons is the first time he has been away
from home. Part of the reason why he finds it so stressful
is the contrast between Michael's family and his own.
What type of family are the Middletons? How do they
differ from Neil and his mother? Imagine a meeting
between the two mothers some time after the holiday and
role-play their conversation.

**2** In the story, particularly at the beginning, Neil keeps
hearing his mother's voice in his head. The author shows
us this voice by writing in italics. At the end of the story,
Neil has changed a little. Write a paragraph which
describes him meeting his mother on his return home.
Consider the questions she would ask him. How much
would he tell? Include his unspoken thoughts by using the
device of writing in italics.

**3** Write the extract from Neil's diary which covers the
incident where he makes his 'excuse' for not going
swimming. Include the reaction of Michael and his family.
Write a later extract after he has visited Mrs Wan and she
has told him, 'Watch that you don't suffer from more than
just the disease.'

### Comparative task

All stories have one or more themes. Rearrange the stories

in this anthology according to the themes you have found in them. Present this as a new Contents page and write a brief introduction explaining your choices.

## Stradbroke Island

Years ago, my family – my Aboriginal family – lived on Stradbroke Island. Years before the greedy mineral seekers came to scar the landscape and break the back of this lovely island. I recall how we used to make the trip to Point Lookout. My father would saddle our horses at early light and we would make our way along the shoreline, then cut inland to climb over the hills covered with flowering pines, wattles and gums. The brumbies would watch our approach from a safe distance. These wild horses never trusted man, their foe . . .

The island is different now . . . Motorcars belch fumes over the island and the noise of industry drowns out all other sounds of life.

*Oodgeroo Nunukul*

# The authors

........................

**Mikhail Afanasevich Bulgakov** (1891–1940), a Russian writer, was born in the city of Kiev, Ukraine. He qualified as a doctor in 1916 and, because of the war, was drafted immediately to a remote country hospital. Apart from feeling that he was learning to swim by being thrown into the deep end, he felt caught between two cultures 500 years apart in time. Later he gave up medicine to write. His part-autobiographical, part-fictional stories based on this early experience were published in magazines and only compiled into *A Country Doctor's Notebook* years after his death.

**Nancy Chong** (1955– ) is a Toronto writer whose father emigrated from China in 1913, ten years before the Canadian Government stopped immigration from China. Her mother, from rural China, came to Canada two years after the Exclusion Act was repealed in 1949. Nancy Chong's autobiographical stories, exploring her intercultural identity, have been published as part of a New Writers' Initiative.

**Anita Desai** (1937– ) was born in Mussoorie, India, of a Bengali father and German mother. She was educated in Delhi and now lives in Bombay. She is well known internationally, writing novels and short stories for adults and young people. Her novel, *The Village by the Sea*, portraying a vivid picture of poverty and wealth in India, has been televised and won The Guardian Fiction Award.

**E. B. Dongala** (1941– ) was born in the Congo and is a poet, novelist and short-story writer as well as a chemistry lecturer at the Universities of Strasbourg and Brazzaville. He has been described as one of Africa's leading satirists and his collection of stories, *Jazz et vin de palme*, which includes *The Man*, was banned in the Congo.

**Julius Lester** (1939– ) was born in St Louis, Missouri, USA. He has been a columnist, folk singer, broadcaster, photographer and university professor. His book, *To be a Slave*, was the first to open out for young readers hidden Black American history and the devastating experience of slavery. A great storyteller who has found and told many tales from the African–American past, he knows that 'Stories can be changed, and should be, as the storyteller feels.'

**Alecia McKenzie** (1960– ) grew up in Kingston, Jamaica, before university study in the USA. She has written for several national and international newspapers. Her first collection of stories, *Satellite City*, which includes *Full Stop*, won the 1993 Commonwealth Literature Prize for Caribbean First Books. She teaches at the Free University in Brussels.

**Bernard MacLaverty** (1945– ) was born in Belfast, Northern Ireland and now lives on Islay, off the west coast of Scotland. His first book, *Secrets and Other Stories*, won a Scottish Arts Council Award. His novels, *Lamb* and *Cal*, have been made into films.

**Millie Murray** (1958– ) was born in the East End of London of Jamaican parents. She has been a nurse, studied drama, worked for BBC Schools TV and writes 'sitcoms' for radio. She has written six novels and works a lot in schools, libraries and colleges.

**Beverley Naidoo** (1943– ) was born in Johannesburg, South Africa and came to England in 1965. She was unable to return freely to South Africa until 1991 and her book, *Journey to Jo'burg*, was banned in South Africa until the lifting of apartheid laws. She has written a number of books for young people, including *No Turning Back*, short-listed for The Guardian Fiction Award, and works also as an Education Adviser and a writer-in-school.

**R. K. Narayan** (1907– ) was born in Madras, South India. Many of his novels and stories are set in the fictional territory of Malgudi, including *An Astrologer's Day*. But, as Narayan says, he can detect Malgudi characters 'even in New York'. Graham Greene described him as 'the novelist I most admire in the English language'.

**Oodgeroo Nunukul** (1920–93), formerly Kath Walker, spent her childhood on Stradbroke Island. Her book, *Stradbroke Dreamtime*, from which *Kill to Eat* is taken, records her own childhood as well as new and old stories within Aboriginal folklore tradition. She was active in presenting the case of dispossessed Aborigine people to the Australian and other world governments.

**Ken Saro-Wiwa** (1941–95), writer and human rights' activist, was hanged by the Nigerian military regime with eight other Ogoni activists in November 1995 despite international protests. They had campaigned against environmental pollution and exploitation by oil companies of the Ogoni region. He had decided to give up writing and concentrate on political campaigning at the time of his death.

**Karl Sealy** (*c.* 1932– ) was born in Barbados. He is a storywriter, poet and critic. His work has appeared in several anthologies and Caribbean journals, including the magazine *Bim*.

**Marion Strachan** (1945– ) was born into a Welsh-speaking family in North Wales and says that as a child she 'wrote stories, poems, plays, and whole newspapers, none of which any one else ever read'. She now runs a library in a secondary school in Dorset.

**Mildred D. Taylor** was born during World War Two in Jackson, Mississippi, USA but her father moved the family north to get away from the racist segregation of the American South. Her writing for young people is drawn from her family's history. She won the Newbery Award with her novel, *Roll of Thunder, Hear My Cry*.

# Further reading

## General collections

*Free As I Know* edited by Beverley Naidoo (1987)
*Somehow Tenderness Survives: Stories of Southern Africa*
    edited by Hazel Rochman (1992)
*Stories from Africa* selected by Madhu Bhinda (Longman
    1996)
*Stories from Asia* selected by Madhu Bhinda (Longman
    1992)
*Stories from Europe* selected by Geoff Barton (Longman
    1996)

## Individual authors

*Basket-ball Game* by Julius Lester (1995)
*Chain of Fire* by Beverley Naidoo (Longman Literature
    1991)
*Dreamtime: Aboriginal Stories* by Oodgeroo Nunukul
    (1995)
*The Friendship and Other Stories* by Mildred D. Taylor
    (1991)
*Kiesha* by Millie Murray (1988)
*Lady A, a Teenage DJ* by Millie Murray (1988)
*Lamb* by Bernard MacLaverty (Longman Literature 1991)
*Malgudi Days* by R. K. Narayan (1984)
*No Turning Back* by Beverley Naidoo (1995)
*The Peacock Garden* by Anita Desai (1991)
*Roll of Thunder, Hear My Cry* by Mildred D. Taylor (1980)
*The Village by the Sea* by Anita Desai (1984)

Addison Wesley Longman Limited
*Edinburgh Gate, Harlow*
*Essex CM20 2JE, England*
*and Associated Companies throughout the world*

© Addison Wesley Longman Limited 1997

This educational edition first published 1997
Third impression 1998

*Editorial material set in 10/12.5 pt Stone Sans*
*Produced by Longman Singapore Publishers (Pte) Ltd*
*Printed in Singapore*

ISBN 0 582 28929 7

Cover illustration by Matthew Richardson

The publisher's policy is to use paper manufactured from
sustainable forests.

## Acknowledgements

We are grateful to the following copyright holders for permission to reproduce
short stories.

Addison Wesley Longman for 'Full Stop' from Satellite City by Alecia McKenzie
(Longman Caribbean Writers, 1992); Addison Wesley Longman on behalf of Saros
International Publishers for 'Robert and the Dog' by the late Ken Saro-Wiwa from A
Forest of Flowers (Longman African Writers Series, 1995). Copyright © Saros
International Publishers, 1995; the author's agent on behalf of the author for
'Circus Cat Alley Cat' by Anita Desai. Copyright © Anita Desai, 1980; Victor
Gollancz Ltd for 'The Gold Cadillac' from The Friendship and Other Stories by
Mildred D Taylor, HarperCollins Publishers Ltd for 'More than just the Disease' by
Bernard MacLaverty from Scottish Short Stories 1983; HarperCollins Publishers
Australia for 'Kill to Eat' from Stradbroke Dreamtime by Oodgeroo Nunukul; The
Harvill Press for 'The STeel Windpipe' from A Country Doctor's Notebook by Mikhail
Bulgakov (First published in Great Britain by Collins and The Harvill Press 1975. The
paperback edition first published by Collins Harvill 1990). Translation © Michael
Glenny 1975; Les Editions Hatier for 'The Man' by E B Dongola from Jazz et Vin de
Palme, Collection Monde Noir Poche. Copyright © Hatier, 1982; the author's agent
for 'Why Apes Look Like People' from Black Folktales by Julius Lester. Copyright ©
Julius Lester 1970; the author, Millie Murray for 'The Escape' (first published in
1987 by The Women's Press Ltd in Watchers and Seekers: Creative Writing by Black